INDUSTRIAL GWYNEDD

GWYNEDD DIWYDIANNOL

Cyfrol/Volume 3 : 1998

Editor/golygydd:

Dr David Gwyn

Gwynedd Archaeological Trust/Ymddiriedolaeth Archaeolegol Gwynedd

Editorial board/bwrdd golygyddol:

Griff Jones
Cae Clyd, Blaenau Ffestiniog

Dr Michael Lewis
Department of History, University of Hull

Dr Gwynfor Pierce Jones
Tal y Sarm

Gareth Haulfryn Williams, MA, DAA, JP
Assistant Director: Culture, Gwynedd County Council/Cyfarwyddwr Cynorthwyol: Diwylliant, Cyngor Sir Gwynedd

Andrew Davidson, BA
Gwynedd Archaeological Trust/Ymddiriedolaeth Archaeolegol Gwynedd

Notes on the contributors/nodiadau ar y cyfrannwyr:

Brodor o 'hen ddinas y glaw' yw **Steffan ab Owain,** cyn-chwarelwr Llechwedd. Wedi ennill gradd yng Ngholeg y Brifysgol, Bangor, dechreuodd gyrfa newydd gyda Gwasanaeth Archifau Gwynedd.

Professor R. Merfyn Jones is author of *The North Wales Slate Quarrymen 1874-1922*, and is Pro-Vice-Chancellor of the University of Wales, Bangor. **Dr Jill Lovecy** is Lecturer in Government at the University of Manchester.

Dr Gwynfor Pierce Jones is an Industrial Archaeology consultant, and lives in Tal y Sarn. **Peter Lord** is Pilcher Senior Research Fellow at the University of Wales Centre for Advanced Welsh and Celtic Studies at Aberystwyth. The most recent of his many books and articles on the visual culture of Wales is *Industrial Society*, published by the University of Wales in 1998.

Ian Manning, a senior chemistry laboratory technician at the University of the West of England, Bristol, is a member of the Broad Gauge Society and is interested in British broad gauge railways of the period 1835 to 1892.

Dr Michael Lewis is Senior Lecturer in the Department of History, University of Hull.

Distributed by Plateway Press, Taverner House, East Harling, Norfolk

Designed and printed by Postprint, East Harling, Norfolk

ISBN 1 871980 42 9

EDITORIAL / GOLYGYDDOL

The people of Wales have recently assumed a new set of responsibilities by electing an Assembly with powers covering a wide range of issues, including heritage. What implications this will have for the promotion and study of industrial history remains to be seen, but some possibilities have already been voiced – statutory agencies such as Cadw and the Royal Commission, though overwhelmingly English in composition, have increasingly acknowledged the distinctiveness of Wales's industrial past, and the National Museum and Galleries of Wales is exploring the idea of a visitor centre based around the idea of 'Wales – the First Industrial Nation.' It would be a pity if, in the midst of this rush to nationhood, the regional dimension of Welsh history and experience were to be ignored, either by the powers-that-be in the Assembly and Cardiff or by local government. Within the last few years, much has been lost in Gwynedd alone, and more is at risk if we persist in seeing the remains of industry exclusively in terms either of capital return or as derelict sites. Inward investment in the shape of the 'Ardal y Lechen' initiative or the attainment of Objective 1 status pose their own problems, and it is imperative that the mistakes made by the WDA in South Wales are not repeated in the north. Wales is a community of communities, with strong, often divergent, often inter-related traditions of industry and work, as well as of language and cultural identity. The economic and technical self-sufficiency of Gwynedd-Môn-Aberconwy in the nineteenth century underlies the region's strong sense of itself now, in the last years of the twentieth; our best hope for the future is to understand the local forces, industrialisation amongst them, that have shaped us in our history.

Contents/Cynnwys

Abbreviations/talfyriadau

The following abbreviations are standard:

Arch. Camb.:	*Archaeologia Cambrensis*
BL:	British Library, Russell Square, London
CCHChSF:	*Cylchgrawn Cymdeithas Hanes a Chofnodion Sir Feirionydd*
CLlGC:	*Cylchgrawn Llyfrgell Genedlaethol Cymru*
CRO:	Caernarfon Record Office, Victoria Dock, Caernarfon, Gwynedd
DRO:	Dolgellau Record Office, Dolgellau, Gwynedd
GAG:	Gwasanaeth Archifau Gwynedd
GAS:	Gwynedd Archives Service
JMHRS:	*Journal of the Merionethshire Historical and Record Society*
LlGC:	Llyfrgell Genedlaethol Cymru, Aberystwyth
LlRO:	Llangefni Record Office, Shire Hall, Llangefni, Ynys Môn
NLW:	National Library of Wales, Aberystwyth
NLWJ:	*National Library of Wales Journal*
PCB:	Prifysgol Cymru, Bangor
PRO:	Public Record Office, Kew/Chancery Lane, London
TAAS:	*Transactions of the Anglesey Antiquarian Society*
TCHS:	*Transactions of the Caernarvonshire Historical Society*
TCHNM:	*Trafodion Cymdeithas Hynafiaethwyr a Naturiaethwyr Môn*
TCHSG:	*Trafodion Cymdeithas Hanes Sir Gaernarfon*
UWB:	University of Wales, Bangor

Front cover:
The Dorothea Quarry, *by an unknown artist*

Y Gyllell Fach

gan Steffan ab Owain

Fel hanes amryw o arfau chwarelyddol eraill, credaf fod hanes datblygiad y gyllell fach yn bur ddiddorol ac yn werth ei adrodd. Pa fodd bynnag, cyn i mi ddechrau ar drafod ei hynt a'i helynt ar hyd y blynyddoedd, efallai y byddai'n syniad da diffinio yn gyntaf oll beth yn union yw 'cyllell fach'.

Erfyn tebyg o ran ffurf i gyllell gyffredin yw'r gyllell fach, gyda llafn o haearn yn amrywio yn ei hyd o naw modfedd hyd at droedfedd a hanner. Fel rheol, gwneid y carn o bren, ac ochr finiog y llafn o ddur. Defnyddir y gyllell gan y chwarelwr i naddu fel y dywedir, 'slgodion o lechfaen. Efallai y dylwn nodi yma hefyd, gall yr enw ar y gyllell newid o un ardal chwarelyddol i'r llall. Dyma rai o'r enwau eraill a ddefnyddid amdani – 'cyllell bach', 'cyllell gerrig', 'cyllell law', a 'cyllell naddu'. Dylid dweud fod cychwyniad rhagflaenydd y gyllell fach yn ôl pob tebygrwydd, yn mynd ym mhell iawn yn ôl mewn hanes. Yn wir, mae rhai o'r farn bod gan 'llechdowyr' cynharaf Prydain, a ddyddia o'r Cyfnod Rhufeinig, ryw fath o erfyn i dirn eu cerrig to pan osodid hwy ar doeau eu hadeiladau. Ond cofier, os oeddynt yn meddu rhywbeth o'r fath mae'n bur debyg mai math o fwyell (*hatchet*) a ddefnyddid at y gwaith hwn – ac nid cyllell naddu soffistigedig fel eiddo'r chwarelwr diweddar. Pa fodd bynnag, ar hyn o bryd ychydig iawn o dystiolaeth sydd gennym parthed cerrig to (o lechfaen) a gafodd eu trin gydag erfyn o'r fath yn y Cyfnod Rhufeinig.

O ddod ychydig yn nes at ein dyddiau ni, ac i'r Oesoedd Canol, yn enwedig o tua'r drydedd, a'r bedwaredd ganrif a'r ddeg ymlaen, gallwn ddweud gyda mwy o sicrwydd fod gan y llechdowyr, fel y rhai a fu'n toi adeiladau yng nghastell Coleshill yn yr hen Sir Fflint (tua 1282), Caernarfon (1317), a Chaerdydd (1316) ryw fath o 'honfas' neu fwyell i naddu'r cerrig tô.

Rai canrifoedd yn ddiweddarach, yn yr ail ganrif a'r bymtheg, cawn yn y gyfrol *Academy of Armory* gan Randle Holme[1] restr ddiddorol o 'Slaters working tools'. Yn eu plith cawn y canlynol:

'A slaters Hatchet
A Trowel
A Hewing Knife to cut the slates even and square
A Hewing Block, any square piece of Wood or Stone to cut the slates upon.'

O edrych drwy'r rhestr hon, mae'n rhaid gofyn, o leiaf, dau gwestiwn. Yn gyntaf, pa mor bell yn ôl mewn hanes y dechreuodd y 'llechdowyr' ddefnyddio'r arfau hyn? Ac yn ail, ai o'r 'slaters hatchet' y datblygodd y gyllell fach, yntau a'i o'r gyllell gyffredin? Ar hyn o bryd, nid allaf ateb y cyntaf. Sut bynnag, credaf bod yr esboniad canlynol a rydd Hugh Derfel Hughes yn taflu dipyn o oleuni ar y mater olaf.

Y gorchwyl nesaf gyda y clytiau oedd eu trwsio a'u hollti; ac yr oedd gan y naddwr gareg deirongl a elwid *Maen nâdd*, ac wrth ei thalcen swp o geyryg, ar yr hwn yr oedd torch wellt, lle yr eisteddai i naddu; nid at yr yn

[1] Randle Holme, *Academy of Armory* (Chester, 1688) p.245

Plat 1
Cerflun gan Richard Westmacott yn eglwys Llandygái, yn ymddangos chwarelwr cynnar Cae Braich y Cafn.

hyd na lled penodol, ond at *ryw* faint, cymaint ac a oddefai y gareg, ac ar y towr druan y disgynai y gwaith o orphen eu cymwyso. Yr oedd amryw o'r llechi hyn yn dri chwarter modfedd, ac weithiau yn fodfedd o dew, ac y mae engreifftiau dyddan i'w cael o honynt weithiau mewn hen furddynod. Nid oedd yr hen gyllell naddu nemor fwy na thriwal; rhywbeth fel saith modfedd a haner o hyd wrth bedair a haner o led, fel y dengys yr engraifft o un sydd yn llaw y ddelw fynor o lechnaddwr sydd yn eglwys Llandegai, ac y mae un arall lled debyg yn Ogwen Bank. O'r diwedd, fel yr oedd y gelfyddyd o naddu a thoi yn gwella, daeth yn amcan, ac yn drefn gan y naddwr i'w lled gyfateb i haner ei hyd, ac wrth ysgil y diwyg hwnw dyfeiswyd trafael haiarn, yr hon ar y dechre nid oedd fwy nag 16 modfedd o hyd, yr hon a osodid mewn mainc; a dyna ddechreuad y Fainc drafael. Dyfeiswyd hefyd i garn y gyllell naddu daflu ychydig allan mewn trefn i ddiogelu bawd y naddwr, pan nad oedd ar y dechre ond sêth fel cleifar. Toc deuwyd i ddeall y gwerth o ddurio y gyllell, â'r drafael, ac yr oedd y llechnaddwr yn ystyried ei hun yn lled gywrain erbyn hyn.[2]

Efallai mai r̂wan yw'r amser gorau i sôn am weddnewidiad arall a ddaeth i'w rhan rywdro yn chwedegau'r ganrif ddiwethaf. Dywedir mai yng Nghloddfa'r Coed, un o chwareli Dyffryn Nantlle, y

digwyddodd hyn, ac ar ôl i 'Sion y Gof', sef John Jones, neu 'Ioan Eifion', (1839-1909) fel y'i gelwid gan amryw y pryd hynny, lunio gwelliant ar y 'gafael' a fyddai ar yr hen gyllell fach. Gyda llaw, adnabyddid ef mewn cyfnod diweddarach fel y Parchedig John Jones, gweinidog gyda'r Bedyddwyr. Mewn traethawd difyr yn dwyn y teitl 'Ysgrifennu yr Hunangofiant goreu' a dderbyniwyd yng nghystadleuaeth Cylchwyl Lenyddol a Cherddorol Brynaerau, Chwefror 1 a'r ail 1929, cyfeiria un yn galw ei hun yn 'Adgof uwch Anghof' at y ddiwygiad uchod. Disgrifia yn y rhan gyntaf o'i draethawd ddyddiau ei lencyndod, a'i flynyddoedd cynharaf fel rybelwr yn y chwarel, ac yna â'i ymlaen i ddweud mai 'Yr adeg yma y dyfeisiodd 'Ioan Eifion' y gyllell a'r gafael gosod' - a byth wedyn nid oes neb yn iwsio un a'r "gafael sownd". Mae'n haws ei dal hi'n sad - ac hefyd i beidio cael "slap bymtheg" - taro dros y "Drafael".'

Yr hyn a olyga'r hen chwarelwr wrth y term 'gafael sownd' ar y gyllell yw, bod yr haearn a wneid hi ohono, yn un darn cyfan o ben blaen y llafn hyd at ei charn. Yr hyn a feddylir wrth y term 'gafael gosod' yw gafael wedi cael ei glensio, neu ei sgriwio) yn sownd ar y rhan o'r gyllell lle cydir ynddi. Wrth gwrs, roedd gan y ddau afael 'dafliad allan' fel i ddiogelu bawd y naddwr.

Er i'r gyllell fach â'r gafael gosod ennill poblogrwydd ymhlith y chwarelwyr, nid yw'n hollol gywir i ddweud, fel y gwna'r traethodwr, ei bod wedi disodli'r gyllell â'r gafael

[2] Hugh Derfel Hughes, *Hynafiaethau Llandegai a Llanllechid* (Bethesda, 1866; ail- argraffwyd y Groeslon, 1979) t. 120.

sownd yn gyfangwbl, chwaith. Na, bu peth ddefnydd ar 'gyllell bach gafael sownd' am flynyddoedd wedyn, yn enwedig yn chwareli Sir Gaernarfon. Eto, mi wn am un neu ddau o dowyr sydd yn dal i ddefnyddio rhai heddiw.

Pa fodd bynnag, trwy lunio gafael newydd ar y gyllell fach, llwyddwyd i arbed aml i darawaid brwnt ar fysedd, a bawd y naddwr. Yn ddiamau, hwyluswyd y gwaith o naddu gyda'r gyllell yn ogystal, ac mewn rhai achosion, bu codiad sylweddol yn y 'sist', sef cynnyrch diwrnod a chwarelwr.

Mae'n ymddangos nad y gafael yn unig a boenai rhai o naddwyr y gyllell fach. Teimlai ambell un, yn enwedig os oedd yn digwydd symud o un ardal chwarelyddol i'r llall i ddilyn ei alwedigaeth, fod maint llafn y gyllell naddu yn gallu bod fel 'maen am ei wddf', fel petae. Un a brofodd hynny, am ysbaid, beth bynnag, oedd un â'r ffugenw 'Ab

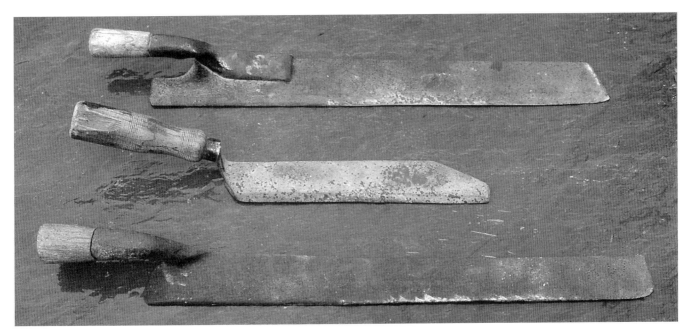

Plat 4 *Amrywiaeth o gyllyll yn Amgueddfa Lechi, Llanberis.*

Owain' (na, nid yr ysgrifennwr presennol mohono) a ddechreuodd weithio yn y chwarel pan oedd yn ddeuddeng mlwydd oed. Oddeutu saith mlynedd yn ddiweddarach, gadawodd ei ardal enedigol ym Methesda, a'i gwaith yn Chwarel Cae Braich y Cafn, a dod i letya yn i ardal Glan y Pwll ym Mlaenau Ffestiniog gyda'r gobaith o gael ei gyflogi yn un o chwareli'r cylch. Disgrifia ei ddiwrnodau cyntaf fel chwarelwr yn 'Stiniog:

> ... cefais air i fyned i Bonc y Shiafft yr Rhiw erbyn 6 o'r gloch boreu Gwener, yr hon oedd a'r safle ar dop y chwarel, yr hon a gyrhaeddais yn brydlon er cyn 6, a chefais fyned i weithio yn lle dyn ieuangc tan hanner dydd Sadwrn, a'r gwaith ydoedd naddu gyda'r gyllell bach, pe un fechan hefyd. Yr oedd yn llawer hwy na'r un a arferaswn yn flaenorol, yr hyn y gwyr pob chwarelwr am yr anfantais o naddu gyda chyllell anghynefin.[3]

Dyma rhai engreifftiau o hydau llafnau cyllell bach a fesurwyd gennyf:

ardal Ffestiniog	1' 5¼" o hyd
Dyffryn Nantlle	1' 5⅛"
Dinorwig	1' 5"
Chwarel Penrhyn	9¼"

Mae'n eithaf posib fod pob un o'r enghreifftiau hyn, a llafn dipyn hwy yn wreiddiol, ond bod traul ac ysiad wedi bwyta ychydig oddi arnynt. Anodd fyddai gadael yr ymdriniaeth hon ar wahanol hydau ein cyllill naddu heb gynnwys ynddi y dyfyniad canlynol:

When the fine splitter with his wooden mallett bound with iron, and his thin chisles, and when the dresser, sitting on a wooden bench on which is fixed a steel knife or frame, with his long knife (which is similar to a blunt sword) and his notched stick with a pike on the end, when both these had finished their work, the result was a finished slate.[4]

Yn wir, mae'n anodd credu weithiau, o gadw'r cyfeiriadau uchod at hyd ein cyllill naddu mewn cof, bod yr hen chwarelwyr wedi dewis enw mor anaddas, 'chyllell fach' o gwbl.

Eto, ar ôl dweud hynna, ceir dau ddywediad chwarelyddol ynglyn â'r 'gyllell naddu', sy'n mwy nag awgrymu, bod dau fath o gyllell ar gael mewn ambell chwarel lle gweithid 'cerrig caled' a 'cherrig meddal.' Dyma nhw: 'gyllath gre at a galad' a'r gyllath ysgafn at y rywiog'. Hyd yn hyn, ac yn bennaf oherwydd prinder 'chwarelwyr y gyllell fach' heddiw, nid wyf wedi llwyddo i gael cadarnhâd gan yr un ohonynt mai cyfeirio at gyllyll o wahanol faint y mae'r dywediadau hyn.

Cipdrem ar hanes y gyllell fach a gafwyd yn yr erthygl uchod; efallai y caf gyfle i son am ei chymar y drafael rhyw dro yn y dyfodol.

In this article, Steffan ab Owain discusses the development and the variations in design of the slate trimming knife, and discusses its relation with tools believed to have been used in the Medieval period.

---

3   Ab Owain, *Hunangofiant Chwarelwr a ysgrifenwyd ganddo ar gyfer Eisteddfod Goronog Chwarelwyr Dorothea a Phen y Bryn i'w chynnal yn yr Assembly Room, Tal y Sarn, 8 Mai 1926.*
4   R. J. Williams, 'Festiniog Slate Quarries', *University of Wales Magazine* 5 (February 1883).

Slate Workers in Wales, France and the United States:

a comparative study

by Professor R. Merfyn Jones and Dr Jill Lovecy

The following article is reprinted from Llafur *Vol. 4 no 4 (1988), by kind permission of the authors and of Neil Evans, editor of* Llafur.

Much of the recent work in the field of mining history has contained an understandable emphasis on regional or local studies. The sheer scale of many extractive industries, and the varying complexities to be discovered within particular coalfields, let alone national aggregates, have not encouraged attempts at formal generalisation and international comparisons. And yet, the comparative method can prove illuminating: in particular it can allow for a highlighting of those factors which result in workers in the same industry, but located in different technological, economic or cultural environments, adopting, at times similar, at times differing patterns of behaviour and action.

The slate industry offers fewer obstacles than many other industries to a comparative treatment, particularly as between the three main producers: France, the United States and Wales. The industry was an economically significant but nevertheless small-scale affair in these countries and, moreover, production in all three countries was at a reasonably comparable level during the industry's most active period at the end of the nineteenth, and the beginning of the twentieth, centuries. In the three countries attempts were made at establishing trade unions for the slate workers and this led to significant industrial relations problems, particularly in the first decade of the twentieth century. The unions which were established, however, differed markedly in structure, and even more so in the political stances they adopted. Several factors can be identified as accounting for these differences and this paper is concerned with locating and discussing those factors.

The economic patterns of differing national developments are clearly of importance but other factors also obtrude into the picture. The organisation of the work

process was crucial as were the associated craft distinctions and, to some extent, related ethnic considerations. The patterns of ownership, and in particular, of economic concentration in the industry, and the general structures of the national labour movements must also be considered. Most importantly, a comparative study of the slate miners of Wales, France and the United States in the period 1870 to 1920 makes it possible for some significant questions to be addressed as to the relative importance of the organisation and economics of production on the one hand, and cultural and political influences on the other, in determining patterns of miners' action and response in these countries.

A geological guide published in 1910 considered the exploitation of slate in thirteen different countries: Britain, France, Austria, Germany, U.S.A., Norway, Portugal, Canada, India, Italy, South Africa, Australia and New Zealand.[1] Slate was primarily used for roofing the vast urban developments of the nineteenth century but it was also used for a variety of other purposes: 'this stone', an American geologist claimed in 1914, 'has become linked with some of the principal necessities of life and death - roofing, flooring, electric switchboards, blackboards, hand slates, billiard and laboratory table tops, vats, tubs, mantels, grave linings, wainscoting, hearths, chimney and well caps, memorial tablets, bread boards, refrigerator shelves, etc."[2] While production was often for local and domestic consumption there did exist a changeable but, at times, not unimportant world market. The three consistently large producers were Wales, France and the United States.

The main centre of British production was the Snowdonia mountains of North Wales, for although slate

---

[1] J. Allen Howe, *The Geology of Building Stones* (1910), pp. 273-326. A world survey published in 1949 also noted significant production in Japan, Spain, Sweden and the Soviet Union; C.H. Behre Jnr, 'Slate' in *Industrial Minerals and Rocks* (American Institute of Mining and Metallurgical Engineers, 1949).

[2] T. Nelson Dale, *Slate in the United States* (Department of the Interior U.S. Geological Survey, Bulletin 586, Washington, 1914), p. 9.

Plate 1 *Women slate splitters in a Belgian quarry.*
CRO XS/1353/24.

the country and abroad. More than half the slate produced in the U.S.A. came from Pennsylvania. Another important slate-field was situated on the Vermont-New York state-line near the town of Granville; there was also some significant production in Maine and, to the south, in Maryland and Virginia.[4]

The somewhat haphazard production of slate in the United States dated back to the mid eighteenth century and the first slate was reportedly mined in Pennsylvania in 1764; as late as the 1850s, however, American production remained at a very low level. Expansion took place over the following three decades and production rose from an estimated 368,000 squares (American production was measured in 'squares', the number of pieces of slate needed to cover 100 square feet of roof) in 1879 to a peak of 1,435,000 squares in 1902.[5] When the Welsh union leader, W. J. Parry, visited America in 1879 he reported that production, and wages, were low and work was hard to find.[6] During the following ten years production doubled and, by 1889 the slate companies were employing over 6,000 men in 212 quarries; 3,600 of them and 105 of the quarries were in Pennsylvania.[7] Stagnation in the early 1890s was followed by rapid growth in 1897 when 'owing to strikes in the Welsh quarries, the U.S.A. gained a foothold again in England and in the English colonies' and exports of American slate leapt from $38,000 in 1895 to $1,370,075 in 1898.[8] Exports declined from then on, at first slowly and then dramatically and the twentieth century pattern of decline seemed to mirror the fate of the slate industry in Wales: no slate was worked in West Bangor, Pennsylvania, one of the main centres of production, after 1946.[9]

In France the main centres of production were near the Belgian border in the Ardennes and in Angers in the department of Maine-et-Loire with production here centred on the town of Trélazé. As in Wales, substantial growth was experienced in the late eighteenth and early nineteenth centuries. By 1847 production in the Angers region had increased five-fold since 1762 and the industry there was employing some 2,500 workers; a similar number was then engaged in the Ardennes. In the second half of the nineteenth century production in Angers continued to expand and, by 1888, the six quarries in Trélazé were employing 5,000 workers and producing 90,000 tons a

was produced elsewhere in the British Isles (in Ballachulish in Scotland, Delabole in Cornwall and in Cumbria as well as in Pembrokeshire), North Wales, with 85% of the total production, dominated the industry. It was, indeed, the major producing area in the world. Even some French slate was marketed as *Galloise*. In the late eighteenth century Welsh slate came to be exploited on a large scale and on a commercial basis. By the boom of the early 1870s approximately 14,000 men worked in the Welsh slate industry, some of them labouring in giant open quarries and others in underground mines.[3] In 1793 North Wales produced some 25,000 tons of slate; by 1877 over 450,000 tons were being produced. Market conditions were depressed throughout the 1880s and the early 1890s but improved towards the end of that decade. Labour problems and the competition from alternative roofing materials then caused serious dislocation and the industry was meeting with increasing problems in the decade leading up to the First World War. In 1918 hardly a quarter of the production of the 1870s was reached and, although there was to be some improvement during the inter-war period, the industry continued to contract. The post-Second World War period witnessed the virtual eclipse of the Welsh slate industry.

In the United States slate was mined or, more typically, quarried, in a dozen states but the main areas of slate production were the 'slate fields' of the eastern seaboard. Slate from here was shipped to supply markets throughout

---

3   See J. Lindsay, *A History of the North Wales Slate Industry* (Newton Abbott, 1974): D. Dylan Pritchard's articles in *The Quarry Managers' Journal* remain the most valuable contribution to history of the industry's economic boom.

4   See Dale, *op. cit.*, and A. T. Coons, 'Slate' in *Mineral Resources of the United States for 1909* (U.S. Geological Survey, 1911), pp. 557-568. See also F.W. Speer, 'Quarry Methods' and N. S. Shaler, 'Descriptions of Quarries and Quarry Regions' in *United States Census, 1880.*

5   Dale, *op. cit.*, (1906 edition), pp. 193-220.

6   W.J. Parry, 'Adroddiad ar ymweliad â chwareli yr Unol Daleithiau', *Chwareli a Chwarelwyr* (1897).

7   'Mineral Industries (Slate)' *United States Census, 1890* (1892) pp. 662-665.

8   Dale, *op. cit.*, (1906 edition), p. 137.

9   J. R. Copeland, 'Delta, Pennsylvania:The Welsh and the Slate Industry', unpublished M.A. thesis (1974).

year. By 1910 French production had expanded to 300,000 tons and there was a total workforce of 9,000, two-thirds of which was employed in the Angers district; a further 1,000 were employed in the Ardennes and 2,500 were scattered in smaller quarries and mines in the Alps, the Pyrenees and Brittany.[10] The French slate industry followed the same path of twentieth century decline, although it seems to have fared rather better in the post war period than the other two countries. One of the largest quarries in Angers, employing 580 men, went into receivership in 1986, decades later than when most of the surviving Welsh quarries ran into difficulties.[11]

The economic history of the industry in the three countries, although differing in significant ways, was, therefore, broadly similar and there was no great disparity between the three nations. Insofar as the world market in slate was concerned, the national producers took advantage of each other's weaknesses and a dovetailing pattern emerged as between the national producers. Trade union development in the three countries, however, followed markedly different paths although, as we shall see, some similarities did emerge.

None of the unions in the industry were particularly strong ones in this period but the most successful was undoubtedly the North Wales Quarrymen's Union (N.W.Q.U.) known as *Undeb Chwarelwyr Gogledd Cymru*, which was also the largest union in the British stone quarrying industry.[12] The history of that union has been discussed at length elsewhere and only a few of the more salient points will be repeated here.[13] The N.W.Q.U. was formed in a wave of successful strikes in 1874 and, although it failed until the First World War to organize more than half of the available quarrymen and slate miners and failed also to establish negotiating machinery with the major employers until that time, it nevertheless did succeed in sustaining continuous organisation until it merged with the Transport and General Workers' Union in 1922/23. This was a considerable achievement as the major employers in the industry became increasingly anti-union in the 1880s and 1890s and made several determined attempts to break the union; these attempts led to dramatic and prolonged industrial confrontations in particular quarries. The N.W.Q.U. leadership was unusual in that a small, radical, middle-class element was prominent until the turn of the century; the founder of, and dominant figure in, the union for much of the nineteenth century was W. J. Parry, a relatively affluent businessman, and his activities

must be placed within the particular political circumstances of Wales at that time. The union organised all workers in the Welsh slate industry irrespective of grade, but made no attempt to organize other stone workers nor to organise slate workers in other parts of Britain.

In 1879 W. J. Parry visited the United States slate fields to assess the possibilities of emigration open to his members. He made no mention, in his subsequent report, of any trade union organisation in what was still a very

Plate 2 *An open pit quarry at Hermitage la Saulie in the Angers, group, showing the chain incline for raising the blocks to the processing level. CRO XS/1072/158.*

---

[10] F. Lebrun, 'Ludovic Ménard et la naissance de syndicalisme ardoisier', *L'Actualité de l'Histoire* No 29 (1959), p. 200 and *passim*. See also A. Noyer, *L'Industrie ardoisière en France* (1934); L. Chaumeil, *L'Industrie Ardoisière de Basse-Bretagne* (Lorient, 1938).
[11] *Le Monde*, 30 Mars 1986.
[12] See *The Royal Commission on Metalliferous Mines and Quarries* Cd.6390, XL1, P.P. 1912-1913.
[13] For a history of the N.W.Q.U. see R. Merfyn Jones, *The North Wales Quarrymen 1874-1922* (Cardiff, 1981).

Plate 3 *Hand-sawing and a treadle-arm slate dresser at an Angers quarry. CRO XS/1072/158.*

small industry.[14] The American slate workers had contributed to his union's funds during the strikes of 1874 but they had no union of their own and the story of trade unionism in the American slate industry is one of relative weakness and division.[15] The bargaining power of skilled slate splitters was, at times, as potentially powerful as that of the organised granite-cutters, who established strong unions in America, but the conditions in the slate industry, the deep divisions between various grades of workers and the industry's unstable economic fortunes, militated against strong and effective organisations.[16]

A short-lived National Slate Quarrymen's Union was formed in 1895 and, over the following two decades, the slate workers' leaders struggled to form a successful union, united but independent of other stone workers. But in the end their attempts ended in failure.[17] In 1903 an International Union of Slate Quarrymen, Splitters and Cutters, which appeared to have links with the General

Slaters' Union of Pennsylvania, was established under the Secretaryship of Robert J. Griffiths. Griffiths aimed to unite all slate workers into one union registered with the American Federation of Labor (A.F.L.). This was a difficult and disputatious enterprise, however, as the different grades already had their own organisations, particularly in Pennsylvania where some quarrymen had their own union, sometimes referred to as the Slate Workers' Union of Pennsylvania. To further complicate matters, some men were already organised in other A.F.L. locals. Griffiths clearly based his organisation on the skilled cutters and splitters; the holemen and millmen had their own organisations and were deeply suspicious of Griffiths and his plans. The AFL's patience was often tried by the divisions between these slate workers, but they did reflect some real differences as well as some purely organisational jealousies. According to one A.F.L. organizer, writing to Griffiths, the holemen were 'too swelled up over the importance of their position in the industry and they look

---

[14] Parry, *op. cit.*

[15] R.T. Berthoff, *British Immigrants in Industrial America* (Boston, 1953), p. 99.

[16] See E. Fenton, 'Italian immigrants in the Stoneworkers' Union', *Labor History*, Spring 1962 pp. 188-207.

[17] This portrait of American slate workers' trade unions is based largely upon the Jurisdictional and International Files of the American Federation of Labor; see also G.M. Fink, *Labor Unions* (Reynolds and Killingsworth, *Trade Union Publications* vol. 1).

upon your people as holding aristocratic ideas as to your importance and skill. That is unfortunate for you as well as them.'

After much acrimony the three main sections of slaters, holemen and millmen were eventually amalgamated following a convention in 1904 and, on 1 January 1905, the International Union of Slate Workers was founded. Griffiths and some other founding officials were removed from office within months of the union's inception and Griffiths became an oppositional dissident within the new organisation. Following further wrangles, the union emerged in 1911 as the American Brotherhood of Slate Workers but, by 1916-17 it was reported to have been ended.

The union's base, and its headquarters, like that of the industry, was in Pennsylvania and, even though it was reported in 1906 that the union had 1150 members in four locales in Vermont, by 1909 all its executive members, except one, were from Pennsylvania. Only the lone delegate from Virginia had a Welsh name. Having failed to build their own independent union, American slate workers seem to have become associated with other stone workers' unions. The Quarry Workers' International Union of North America, founded in 1903, became the United Stone and Allied Products Workers of America in 1941, and merged with the United Steel Workers of America in 1971. Craft and geographical divisions had prevented the American slate workers from building a successful and independent organisation but they did display considerable organisational initiative and persistence and, as we shall see, were involved in some bitter disputes with obstinate employers.

French slate workers played a rather more prominent role in their national labour movement than either of their American or Welsh counterparts, even though they met with only modest local success.[18] The slate workers of Angers, in particular, in spite of their relatively small number, were important catalysts in the development of French mining trade unionism. Under the Second Empire two Trélazé slate splitters, in a spectacular revolutionary outburst, had led some five or six hundred slate workers in an ill-fated march on Angers to proclaim *La République démocratique et socialiste*. There followed a long period of quiescence. However, from 1890 onwards the slate workers of Angers were to build and sustain union organisation through a series of long and bitter confrontations with their employers, culminating in the decade 1903-1913, when the militancy of the slate workers both reflected and fed into the ascendancy of revolutionary syndicalism over the mainstream of organized trade unionism in France: the *Confédération Générale du Travail,* (C.G.T.) founded in 1895.

Crucially, from the outset, the leading militants in the Angers industry, almost all of them skilled workers, strove to create an industrial union and to unite all sections of the workforce despite the sharp divisions created by the pattern of work organisation. This contrasted strongly with the experience of the Ardennes where splitters, organised into a craft union, opposed the admission of the underground workers' union to the *Fédération des Travailleurs Socialistes* to which they themselves belonged. In Angers, however, in 1890, six years after trade unionism had been legalised in France, an effective united organisation did come into being which owed a good deal to the energetic leadership of Ludovic Ménard, a skilled slate splitter who combined a fierce belief in libertarian socialism with a strong tactical sense.

The new *Syndicat Ardoisier* had 1,000 members by the time of its first annual meeting in 1891. Its programme appealed to all sections of the workforce but, despite some partial victories in strikes in 1890 and in a particularly violent dispute in 1891, the union faced many problems, including internal wrangles about socialist doctrine. Defeat in a major lock-out in 1897 left the union weak but the leaders re-grouped from 1901 and, in 1904, founded, with slate workers in Brittany, the *Fédération Nationale des Ouvriers Ardoisiers*. This union affiliated to the C.G.T. and voted for the revolutionary syndicalist Charter of Amiens in 1906.

In 1907 slate workers from the Ardennes and the Alps affiliated and, in 1910, the Pyrenees slate workers also joined, thus creating a truly national organisation. The leaders set themselves the aim of expanding from this base in the slate industry and creating one union for all extractive and underground workers in France, thus overcoming the deep political differences between rival miners' unions. In Maine-et-Loire gold and iron-ore miners joined them, as did some coal miners nationally; negotiations with the Miners' Federation of the C.G.T. led, in 1910, to the creation of the *Fédération Nationale des Travailleurs du Sous-sol et Similaires*. Success in winning legislation to extend to them the special provisions won by coal miners in 1894 (pensioned retirement at 55) and 1905 (the eight-hour day) eluded them, however, until after the First World War. In 1919 legislation gave the eight hour day to all workers and in 1920 a special bill gave slate workers the same retirement rights as coal miners.

---

[18] This account of trade unionism in France relies heavily on Lebrun, *op. cit.;* M. Poperen, *Un Siècle de Luttes au Pays de l'Ardoise* (Anjou 1972) and *Syndicats et Luttes Ouvrières au Pays d'Anjou* (n.d.); for the Ardennes region, see H. Manceau, *Des Luttes Ardennais* (n.d.); there are also interesting comments and statistics in P.N. Stearns, *Revolutionary Syndicalism and French Labor: a Cause without Rebels* (1971).

Slate Quarry, Granville, N.Y.

Plate 4 *A slate quarry at Granville, New York State, showing a ropeway system.*   *Courtesy of Dr Gwynfor Pierce Jones.*

French slate workers did not establish the sort of resilient trade union organisation to be found in North Wales, and membership of their organisation was often dismally low, but they, from the 1890s, survived as a trade union despite bitter struggles and, more important, were able to extend the influence of their organisation to other extractive industries and help create an industrial union for all extractive workers.

As we have seen, therefore, trade union development in France, Wales and the U.S.A. followed quite different paths; to some extent this reflected different political and cultural environments but it also resulted from the different ways in which slate workers in the three countries reacted to similar problems in the quarries and mines. One

important determinant affecting the degree and nature of organisation amongst slate miners was the widespread disparity between the size of various concerns. In the United States, few units of production were very large and, in 1889, the average quarry employed only twenty workers (some concerns were, of course, larger than this). Patterns of ownership are difficult to establish but all the companies appear to have been relatively small, and certainly none approached the size of some of the Welsh and French producers. The difficulties encountered by trade unionism in America were clearly linked, to a significant degree, to this absence of major producers. In both Wales and France trade union organisation came to be rooted in areas of greatest concentration of production even though smaller units could also harbour union activity.

In Wales, half the 14,000 workforce in the 1890s worked in just three massive concerns: the Penrhyn and Dinorwic quarries (which employed approximately 3,000 each) and the Oakeley slate mine.[19] Trade unionism was much more firmly established in Dinorwic and Penrhyn than elsewhere and it was in these quarries that set-piece labour disputes took place. In France a quite distinctive pattern of industrial concentration was achieved, particularly in the Angers district, where the Prefect of the department engineered in the 1820s the creation of what was effectively a cartel organisation, the *Comission des Ardoisières d'Angers*. Towards the end of the century the joint activities organised by the *Comission* catalysed a further process of industrial concentration when six of the original companies (four of them with quarries in Trélazé) created a single giant company in 1891 and the 1890s witnessed further concentration and an effective division of the industry between two powerful companies. The influence thus amassed by the major employers created enormous difficulties for trade unionism but this also served as a stimulus to trade union action and it was in these quarries that effective organisation for the workforce dramatically emerged.

A further determinant in affecting union development was the organisation of the work process. The difference between the main methods of extracting slate - underground mining on the one hand, and the open cast methods of the quarries on the other - did not seriously affect the patterns of labour (although different legal measures did apply); but differences in wage and craft structures were important. Slate production everywhere was remarkably labour-intensive and, in the period under review, technological changes did not radically change this. The main reason for this was that slate was not an extractive business only; once the rock had been won from

---

[19] For a discussion of this issue and others, see R. Merfyn Jones, *op. cit.*, chapter 3 and *passim.*

the ground it then had to be sawed, dressed and split into actual roofing slates; this processing of the raw-material extracted from the quarry or mine was usually conducted on the mine-top in sheds or mills. The splitting of the slates themselves was by hand and was everywhere considered to be particularly skilled work. The slate workforce therefore consisted in all countries, not only of managers and a number of unskilled labourers but also of two groups of more or less skilled workers: those who extracted the rock itself and those who then processed the rock and manufactured the roofing slates. The relationship between these two main groups was to be crucial in determining the efficacy of trade union organisation in the three countries.

In the Welsh language the same word, *chwarelwr*, was generically used for all quarry workers but, within the industry itself, there was nevertheless a distinction drawn between, on the one hand, the rockman or *creigiwr* who laboured at the rock face and, on the other hand, the slate splitter who abrogated the title *chwarelwr* to himself; other grades - labourers, badrockmen and others - were considered unskilled and hardly worthy of being called *chwarelwyr* at all. These differences between the grades were, however, overcome to a significant degree and the union organised all workers in the industry. The major reason for this relatively successful unity was the wages system in use in the quarries. The bargain system ensured that the differences between the various groups in the quarry were far less corrosive of organisational coherence than was the case in France and particularly in the U.S.A. The bargain system had many features but in this context the key characteristic of this method of determining wages was that the unit or crew which negotiated a monthly bargain with management consisted of both rockmen and slate splitters. The rockmen therefore produced directly for their own partners in the sheds on the surface. This created a system which was extremely difficult to manage but which also tied the fortunes of both groups of slate workers directly together; in Wales, therefore, the very real differences in skill between the two groups resulted in only very marginal differentiation in status. In France and the U.S.A. the situation was very different.

In the United States the distinction between the holemen and the cutters and splitters was much more pronounced. In Pennsylvania the two processes could, at times, be quite separate and some quarries were extractive concerns only, selling their blocks to separate slate mills. In France, although the same local term *les perreyeurs* was used in Angers for all slateworkers, the organisation of work created deep structural divisions, even when the workforce shared the same employer. The splitters or *fendeurs (ouvriers d'à haut* in local parlance) were paid on a piece work basis whilst the miners or *fonceurs* (locally known as the *ouvriers d'à-bas)* were organised into gangs working on six-monthly bargains. A third, unskilled and less well-paid group was formed by the day-labourer *bassicottiers* who worked below loading slate slabs and the *journaliers du jour* who delivered the slabs to the splitters formed the lowest stratum. In both France and the U.S.A. an element of an ethnic division of labour also existed. In Angers the *journaliers du jour* were often Bretons. In Pennsylvania this division was more pronounced, the holemen being Dutch, Cornish, Irish or German whereas the splitters and cutters were often of Welsh descent.[20] In both France and the U.S.A. this basic division in the work force, which itself reflected the processes involved in the production of roofing slates, proved to be a major obstacle to trade union organisation. As we have seen, it needed the fervour of revolutionary syndicalism in Angers to overcome successfully the chasm which existed between *fonceurs* and *fendeurs;* in the Ardennes organisational unity was never achieved. In the United States only a temporary and fragile unity could be created by means of sectional alliance and trade unionism was bedevilled by jealousies.

Intense craft pride existed in all three countries and in Wales the harmful effects of this were only ameliorated by the bargain system. Other features of a craft tradition persisted, particularly the slate workers' fierce sense of independence whilst at work and their consequent resistance to the imposition of managerial prerogatives. In America the basis of the slate workers' independence was further strengthened by a system of virtual sub-contracting. In Angers the splitters' sense of themselves as a craft aristocracy was reinforced by their ability to sustain among themselves well into the century a number of pre-industrial guild practices (banned by Royal decree in 1823), including a complex series of rules for work sharing which centred on reservation of entry into the trade for their own sons (the employers attempted to break these practices in mid-century by introducing, for a period, women workers). It was observed in 1905 that, in Belgian slate mines, *'L'organisation du travail d'abord est telle que l'ouvrier conserve une grande indépendance.'*[21] This was equally true of the three countries discussed here and this fact was central to both the strengths and weaknesses of the trade unions of the slate workers and to the particularly bitter and prolonged industrial disputes which characterised their labour relations in the late nineteenth and early twentieth centuries.

A further common characteristic of the slate industry in all three countries was that they had to contend with

---

[20] For a discussion of Welsh immigrants in the American slate industry, see Berthoff *op. cit.*, pp. 78-79.
[21] E. Savoy, 'Ardoisier du Bassin d'Herbeumont Belgique', *Les Ouvriers des Deux Mondes* (Paris 1905).

Plate 5 *Splitters and dressers at work in a Granville slate quarry. These men may be Ruthenians, who arrived in Granville at the end of the nineteenth century, and took on many of the labouring jobs in the quarries, as Welshmen increasingly took over managerial positions.*
Courtesy of Dr Gwynfor Pierce Jones.

unstable economic conditions. In large measure this was due to the fact that they were producing for the highly volatile building industry. This led to periods of over-production and depression when the building trade was slack, followed by sudden building booms which created demand which the industry could not meet, thus causing customers to look to other suppliers, or to alternative roofing materials. In all three countries the combination of the workers' sense of independence, their craft consciousness and the difficult economic currents, together with the labour-intensive nature of production, forced employers to challenge the alliance of trade unionism in the workplace. This led to some exceptionally bitter and destructive strikes and lock-outs and, despite differences in union and work organisation French, Welsh and American slate workers were, in the closing years of the nineteenth century and the early years of the twentieth, all involved in serious industrial conflict.

In Wales there were major disputes in 1874, 1885 and 1892 which affected different quarries or mines but the most notorious battles took place in one of the two largest concerns, the Penrhyn Quarries near Bethesda. For eleven months in 1896-97, and for a further three years from 1900 to 1903, the union was locked out of the quarry by the aristocratic owner, Lord Penrhyn. The town of Bethesda, the quarry and the Welsh industry were brought to the brink of economic collapse.[22]

The issues which led to this disastrous confrontation, which witnessed unbridled viciousness and military intervention on two occasions, were many and complex but the lock-out was essentially aimed at limiting the power over production exercised by a skilled, organised and politically hostile workforce.

In France disputes started over relatively minor issues were as likely to be quickly translated into class confrontations and turn into long and intransigent battles, as were responses to major employers' offensives mostly aimed at breaking the workers' control of the organisation of their work (such as the 1891 strike and, again in 1910, when the employers attempted to destroy traditional practices of work-sharing). During these disputes quarries

[22] See Jones, *op. cit.*, chapters 7-8.

were occupied by the military, states of siege were declared and crowds cleared by cavalry charges.

Much of this can be accounted for by the employers' determination not to cede any terrain to organised labour and most of the pre-1911 disputes in Angers were responses to managerial offensives. But in 1911, 1912 and 1913 the slate workers themselves went on the offensive with demands for higher wages. The strikes and lock-outs which ensued were extremely bitter and the last mobilisation of the French slate workers before the First World War led to defeat and massive victimisation. Doubtless the character of many of these French strikes were testimony to ill-disciplined organisation but, equally certainly, the revolutionary syndicalist creed also offered the slate workers the immediate perspective of denouement through *la grève générale*.[23]

In the United States the pattern was somewhat different but there were many similarities also. There was a lock-out in Bangor, Pennsylvania, in 1906 and the following year there was a serious and prolonged strike in the Vermont slate district which lasted into 1908. In the same year battle was also engaged in the small slate field of Virginia. The disputes in Buckingham County, Virginia, from 1907 to 1910 bear a striking resemblance to those which broke out in Wales (not least because there was a significant Welsh involvement amongst the men and the employers, even the quarries were called Arvonia) and in France. A long dispute in 1907 over the question of union membership failed to resolve the matter and the dispute flared up again three years later at the Arvonia quarries. The workers produced an appeal which insisted that the dispute was not merely of local interest but was also 'for the benefit of organised labor' as 'we are pitted against one of the most heartless combinations that ever attempted a war of extermination of the labor movement.' The strike lasted through the summer and autumn of 1910 and was characterised by bitter inflexibility on both sides. The A.F.L. organiser who finally achieved a settlement was staggered by the attitudes of both employers and workers. It was, he reported 'one of the most difficult propositions I have ever handled.' Slate workers in Wales or France, however, would have found the circumstances very familiar. The company was out to break the union and the workers themselves displayed an equally determined response which the A.F.L. official considered 'over-zealous' for 'the men thought best to make every demand which occurred to them so as to be prepared to settle up all questions at once and be done with it for all time.'[24]

As we have seen, therefore, the slate industries and slate workers of France, Wales and the U.S.A. shared many common features but, whilst there were some absorbing similarities, there were also striking differences. Despite the elements of variety discussed above, there was, in terms of actual organisational practice, much that was the same in all three countries; independent unions of varying success were established but they all suffered from many weaknesses and all eventually merged with larger organisations of other workers; the distinction between various grades within the industry was significant everywhere as was the presence of intransigent employers. But in their aspirations much separated these workers, and nowhere was this more visible than in the politics of their organisations. The N.W.Q.U. was essentially part of the cross-class late nineteenth century Welsh assault on Conservative landlordism; in Angers it was the liberating vision of revolutionary syndicalism that was to provide the inspiration; in America the several attempts at organisation were all in a tradition of fractious 'laborism'. To seek explanations for these differences we must look outside the workplace to the political cultures of the various countries and to the nature of the available leaderships.

What is noteworthy is that the traditional sense of craft independence, characteristic of all slateworkers, was able to express itself in different forms, forms which were themselves dependent upon the political cultures of their national environments; in the United States this independence readily became individualism and rendered any collective action difficult although far from impossible; in Wales it fed a Victorian trade unionism into the politics of radical awareness; in France it adapted naturally to the idea of workers' autonomy which was at the heart of revolutionary syndicalism. Similar industries, with similar conditions and problems, could thus produce in these different countries workers' organisations which espoused widely divergent strategies and aspirations.

Finally, it is worth noting that what characterised industrial conflict in the three countries considered here was not only a generally weak organisation but also a capacity, at times, for prolonged, violent and bitter confrontations which witnessed a preference for defeat over compromise: in Bethesda and in Trélazé, in Arfon as much as in Arvonia, Buckingham County, slate workers in this period pursued not only trade union grievances but also a desire to 'settle up all questions at once and be done with it for all time.'

---

[23] See Poperen, *op. cit.*; there is a rare Welsh reference to French strikes in *Yr Herald Cymraeg*, 24 Mawrth 1891.
[24] Report of E.C. Davison, Organizer, A.F.L. on Arvonia Strike, Richmond, Virginia, 24 November 1910 to Morrisson, Secretary of the A.F.L. in A.F.L. records, the Samuel Gompers Era, Nat. 11, 2424.

Broad Gauge Rolling Stock at Holyhead Breakwater

by Ian Manning

In *Industrial Gwynedd* Volume 2 an article by Andrew Neale[1] described the building of Holyhead North Breakwater in the nineteenth century which involved the deposition of boulder rubble, using a broad gauge (7' 1/4") railway, to provide a foundation for a massive stone superstructure. This article contains copies of contemporary illustrations of wagons used on the contractors' railway to transport stone from the nearby Holyhead Quarry to the construction site.

A photograph from the Gutch Collection of the National Library of Wales[2] shows two of these wagons in Holyhead Quarry (see Plate 1). Scale drawings appeared in *The Engineer*, 2 February 1867 (see Fig 1), and in a paper, 'Holyhead New Harbour' by Harrison Hayter M.Inst.C.E. in *Proceedings of the Institution of Civil Engineers* (see Fig 2).[3] This latter contains better quality drawings, correctly dimensioned, and provides an exhaustive account of the entire Holyhead North Breakwater project.

To deposit rubble on the sea bed, temporary but substantial staging was first erected on site, consisting of a timber roadway platform of five pairs of longitudinal timber baulks supported on a series of wooden vertical and 'A' piles sunk in place at regular intervals with stone-filled boxes fixed to their lower extremities. The feet of these piles rested on the sea bed to be buried and consolidated by successive coverings of stone. The staging was about 150' wide and, at rail level, approximately 20' above high water mark, the sea depth being 50'-55' at low water.

Quartzite rock, a recrystallised sandstone, from Holyhead Mountain, was principally used for the breakwater foundations. About 4,000 tons was transported and deposited daily, although the maximum quantity moved in any one day was 5,220 tons. The largest amount of rock processed in any one week was 26,164 tons, in a single month, 109,707 tons, and in any one year, 1,066,918 tons. A total of 7,000,000 tons of rubble was used to create these foundations which are about 450' wide on the sea bed, inclining to 250' width at low water mark for a length of about 7,860', exemplifying the colossal scale of operations in building Holyhead North Breakwater.

Messrs Joseph and Charles Rigby were awarded the construction contract initially, with James Meadows Rendel as Engineer-in-Chief but it was George C. Dobson, M.Inst.C.E., site engineer, who designed the wagons. These were mainly fabricated of wrought iron, having a riveted body carried on a stout timber chassis and capable of carrying 8-10 tons of stone. About 250 were assembled for this project. These vehicles were devised to tip boulders directly into the sea through the spaces between the longitudinal timber baulks upon which the broad gauge rails were laid. Essentially the wagon's riveted body contained a moveable wrought iron chute running the full length of the truck's load-carrying compartment, suspended on the vehicle chassis. The tipping section was counterbalanced and able to rotate on pins but was normally kept closed and secure by a latching trigger opening mechanism.

The wagons were loaded at the rock face sidings in Holyhead Quarry, their brakes being locked whilst loading using rail hand cranes, as depicted in Plate 1 (overleaf). The gradients of these sidings were so engineered that, on release of the brakes, each wagon would roll away to the weigh-bridge to record its load and thence along the slightly inclined main line to where the breakwater construction staging joined the shore at Soldier's Point.

At the Soldier's Point siding, these wagons were sorted into short trains of three or four for hauling by steam locomotive to the staging. Presumably, discharge sites would be organised to ensure a clear descent into the sea beneath the wagons so no supporting cross members would be struck and damaged by the boulders. When each trigger mechanism was manually released, the wagon's compartment, under the weight of its load, would rotate on its pins to tip its contents through the space between the baulks into the sea. Being counterbalanced, this section

[1] Andrew Neale, 'Broad Gauge at Holyhead', *Industrial Gwynedd/Gwynedd Diwydiannol* 2 (1997), pp. 18-25.
[2] N.L.W. Gutch collection no. 513/PE2516.
[3] Anon., 'The Holyhead Harbour' in *The Engineer* XXIII (22 February 1867), pp. 151-2, Harrison Hayter M.Inst.C.E., 'Holyhead New Harbour', *Proceedings of the Institution of Civil Engineers* 44, No. 1454, pp 95-130.

Plate 1 *Broad gauge wagons in Holyhead Quarry. Courtesy of NLW, Gutch Collection No. 513/PE2616.*

would quickly return to horizontal to close the trigger mechanism, securing the compartment. Repeatedly depositing stone (in overlapping fashion) throughout the entire breakwater site would eventually establish and consolidate the foundations. Empty wagons would be returned by locomotive to the sidings near Soldier's Point for marshalling into trains of twelve to fifteen vehicles. These were then locomotive-hauled back to the main sidings at Holyhead Quarry. Horses were always used to draw tipping wagons from these main quarry sidings to those at the rock face.

Similar Dobson broad gauge rock tipping wagons were used on other breakwater and harbour installation engineering projects: Portland Breakwater and Harbour Fortifications, Isle of Portland, Dorset, England 1847-1873; Port Erin, Isle of Man 1864-1870; Table Bay Harbour, South Africa *c.*1885; and Ponta Delgada Breakwatwer, Island of São Miguel, in the Azores. (Port Erin Breakwater was eventually completely destroyed by catastrophic storms in 1881 and 1884.)

Contemporary photographs of Dobson-type wagons employed at Port Erin (see Plate 2) do reveal some differences compared with the drawings published in *The Engineer* and *Proceedings of the Institution of Civil Engineers*. In these publications, all the vehicle's wheels were shown as the seven split spoke form while those used at Port Erin had nine-spoke solid cast metal wheels at the brake end of the truck and eight split-spoke type on the other wheelset. There were also differences in the design of brakes and the opening mechanism of these wagons compared with the Holyhead vehicles. Dobson-type wagons built for the Table Bay Harbour project in South Africa by the Gloucester Railway Carriage and Wagon Company Limited in 1885 were fitted throughout with solid metal cast wheel of eight spokes, their brakes and trigger mechanism being similar to those of the Port Erin wagons. Photographs from the Gloucester Railway Carriage and Wagon Company Ltd archive (see Plates 3 and 4 overleaf) show these differences and illustrate the tipping operation (see Plate 3).

Plate 2 *The construction of the Port Erin breakwater, showing Dobson-type wagons. Courtesy Manx National Heritage/Eiraght Ashoonagh Vannin.*

Engineering projects employing specially constructed contractors' railways have often used narrow gauge as opposed to standard 4' 8½" track, curves of tighter radii being more readily facilitated. Why then were the contractors' railways used in the building of Holyhead Breakwater, Portland Breakwater and Fortifications, Port Erin Breakwater, Table Bay Harbour and Ponta Delgada Breakwater all laid to broad gauge?

Construction at all these sites necessitated laying large boulders from railway wagons. The larger the boulder, the greater the weight of stone laid per unit of time, the more economical the exercise and substantial the resulting rubble formation. The gauge of the railway would determine the space available between the longitudinal baulks through which the boulders could drop and hence limit the size of boulder. At Holyhead, this distance was

about 5' 9". Allowing for the same width of baulks, and of rail, a distance of 3' 5½" could be estimated for an equivalent standard gauge system. Therefore, tentatively, the largest boulder accommodated by the broad gauge would have been about 1.6-1.7 (i.e. 69/41.5) times that allowed by a comparable standard gauge version.

Broad gauge railway vehicles were recognised as having a lower centre of gravity compared with those on the standard gauge, resulting in greater stability – of fundamental importance on a marine site timber staging. The weight a mobile railway crane could safely lift without outriggers (additional extended-side supports on levelling screw jacks or temporary packing) was also known to be determined by the gauge. A broad-gauge railway hand-crane could safely lift more than its standard gauge counterpart, without cumbersome outriggers, which might

Plate 3
Dobson-type wagons for the Table Bay Harbour Project.
Courtesy of Gloucestershire Record Office D4791/16/2A.

Plate 4
Dobson-type wagons for the Table Bay Harbour Project.
Courtesy of Gloucestershire Record Office D4791/16/2A.

TIPPING WAGON, HOLYHEAD HARBOUR WORKS
DESIGNED BY MR. W. DOBSON, RESIDENT ENGINEER.

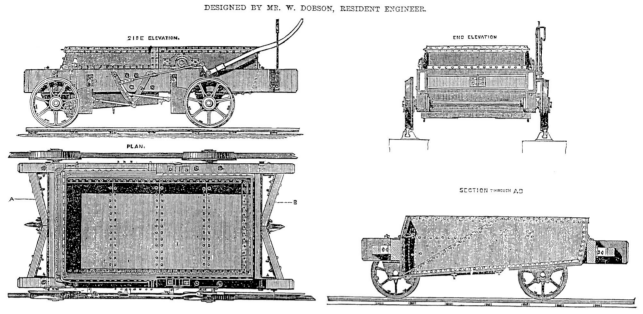

Fig 1 *A scale drawing of Dobson wagons.*   *Courtesy* The Engineer

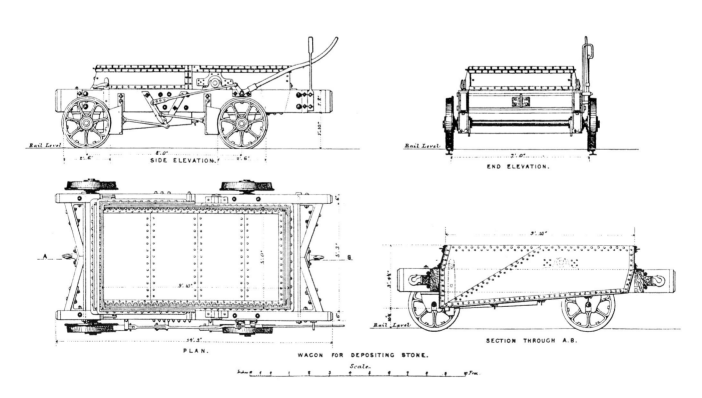

Fig 2 *A scale drawing of Dobson wagons.*   *Courtesy Institution of Civil Engineers.*

compromise a crane's mobility and convenience. Mobile railway cranes were essential in loading quarried stone and in the erection and maintenance of timber staging on the Holyhead Breakwater project.

By 1847 the main lines of the broad gauge Great Western Railway and Bristol and Exeter Railway, engineered by Isambard Kingdom Brunel, had been successfully completed largely using iron rails on longitudinal timbers, so the use of this type of broad gauge baulk road was well established and documented. It provided contractors for the Holyhead breakwater with a tried and tested method of track construction. J. and C. Rigby would have been well acquainted with Brunel's railway construction and practice through their contractual work for the Great Western Railway, including the building of Swindon station in 1841 and the early locomotive works at Swindon in 1842-3.[4]

All these factors clearly favoured the choice of broad gauge at the Holyhead Breakwater, under its engineer-in-chief James Meadows Rendel, and this construction method was readily adopted for other harbour engineering projects where there were similar requirements. Unfortunately, Rendel died in 1856, his place being taken by John Hawshaw, later Sir John Hawshaw, who managed the work to completion, whilst George C. Dobson remained site engineer. Their development of this technique, although long superseded by modern procedures employing coffer dams, made possible some of the most prodigious engineering projects of the nineteenth century.

Acknowledgements

The author wishes to thank the following for their help in supplying information for this article:

Dr David Gwyn, editor of *Industrial Gwynedd*, for kindly drawing the author's attention to the early photograph from the Gutch collection of the National Library of Wales which shows broad gauge contractors' railway rolling stock in Holyhead Quarry.

Mrs Mary Murphy, Archivist, and her staff at the Institution of Civil Engineers, Great George Street, Westminster, London SW1P 3AA, for finding the paper 'Holyhead New Harbour' by Harrison Hayter M.Inst.C.E. in the *Proceedings of the Institution of Civil Engineers* and for kindly supplying a photocopy.

Fellow member of the Broad Gauge Society, Mr Danny Fountain, for details of the early photograph of the construction of Port Erin Breakwater, Isle of Man.

Permission to reproduce copyright photographs from collections of the following is gratefully acknowledged:

The National Library of Wales/Llyfrgell Genedlaethol Cymru

The Gloucester County Record Office

The Manx National Heritage/Eiraght Ashoonagh Vannin.

Thanks are also due to the Institution of Civil Engineers and *The Engineer* for permission to reproduce drawings, which previously appeared in their publications.

---

[4] E.T. MacDermott, *History of the Great Western Railway 1833-1863* volume 1 (revised C.R. Clinker) repr. 1989.

A Painting of Dorothea Quarry

The following article analyses an unsigned painting of Dorothea Slate Quarry in Dyffryn Nantlle. The first section is contributed by Dr Gwynfor Pierce Jones, and considers the painting as evidence for the industrial archaeology of the site. The second, by Peter Lord, discusses the painting within the context of representations of industrial scenes in Wales in the nineteenth century.

Part (I)

by Dr Gwynfor Pierce Jones

Introduction

The Dorothea Slate Quarry is located on the floor of the Nantlle valley, mid-way between the villages of Tal y Sarn and Nantlle. It was in the late nineteenth to mid-twentieth centuries the premier of the twenty or so individual slate quarries which once operated in this district. Employing over 500 men in its heyday, and producing at its high point around 15,000 tons of roofing slates per annum, Dorothea was also one of the most consistently profitable of the second rank of concerns in this industry.

The first excavations on the Dorothea site appear to have been a speculation initiated by a group of local prospectors in the mid-1820s, rather late in comparison with the mid- to late-eighteenth century opening dates for most of the adjacent quarries. The most probable reason for this was the failure to understand the complex geology of the Nantlle district, where opening quarries tended to depend upon the discovery of exposures of the slate rock on hillsides; the Dorothea site comprised the almost flat meadows of Tal y Sarn Uchaf farm, sloping gently down to the northern shore of the lower Nantlle lake.

The initial trial quarry at Dorothea was at the site later called Twll Uchaf (the 'Upper Pit' or 'No.1'), where a slightly steeper slope allowed the excavation of a cutting into the rising ground. The discovery here of a bed of blue slate of commercial value enabled the local men to sell their mineral licence (or 'take-note') to another party, which had the necessary capital required to develop the putative workings into a fully-fledged commercial operation. This purchase of the Dorothea quarrying rights in 1828 by William Turner, a very successful entrepreneur[1] in partnership with his son-in-law, John Morgan (a banker, of Caernarfon), marked the first important turning point in the industrial history of the site.

Turner and Morgan initially concentrated on developing the existing 'No.1' pit, but during their twenty-year tenure, three other workings were also opened on the site. Originally known colloquially as Gloddfa Bach ('the Small Quarry'), later Cloddfa'r Llyn ('the Lake Quarry'), and also as 'Turner's Quarry', by the 1840s the trading title of the concern adopted the name of the widowed owner of the land, Mrs Dorothea Garnons, of Leeswood, Flintshire.[2]

In 1848, the elderly William Turner, apparently unhappy at the stewardship of his business affairs at Dorothea by his son, Thomas, decided to sell his lease of the quarry as a going concern. With an asking price of £3,000, the sale circular described the quarry as ' ... in full operation, worked by steam and water power ... provided with every requisite for the efficient working of it, in Engines, Pumps, Weighing Machines, Sheds, Railroads and Waggons.'[3]

Despite some interest from another party,[4] the successful purchaser was a concern which had the distinction of being the most important contemporary local Welsh joint-stock company. Its advent represents the second important turning point in the quarry's history.

The promoters were a group of quarrymen leasing and working the small nearby Pwll Fanog Quarry. With their entrepreneurial zeal fighting against innate pessimism in taking on such a large concern, a campaign to recruit shareholders was mounted locally amongst their peers,

---

[1]   In origin a Lake District man, who had worked at the Seathwaite slate quarry; on coming to Wales in 1800 he worked Diffwys, Dinorwic, Pen y Bryn and Pen yr Orsedd. See M.J.T. Lewis and M.C. Williams, *Pioneers of Ffestiniog Slate* (Penrhyndeudraeth, 1987) *passim* and Sir Llywelyn Turner, *Memories* (Caernarfon, 1904) *passim*.

[2]   Turner had been in partnership with Dorothea's late husband, Richard, at Pen y Bryn Quarry from 1808-18. See Brynley Jones and Gwynfor Pierce Jones, 'A Plateway in a Nantlle Slate Quarry', *Industrial Gwynedd* 1 (1996).

[3]   CRO: X/Dorothea 911.

[4]   J.W. Greaves, later of Llechwedd, then operating the small Fachwen Quarry in Llanddeiniolen.

including several persons who had undoubtedly amassed a nest-egg as slate carters before the opening of the Nantlle Railway in 1828.

The shares in the new Dorothea concern had a par value of £50 and were sold fully paid-up so as to raise the £1,500 deposit needed to secure the interest of Turner and Morgan. However, the initial rate of sale appeared insufficient to raise the deposit before the set date, probably because men who had risen from poverty to relative wealth were unwilling to risk their gains on a quarry which had been inexplicably closed by one of the most successful entrepreneurs of his day.

Fortunately for the promoters, they were able to involve the Minister of the local Calvinistic Methodist chapel, who had also been a working quarrymen. The Rev. John Jones, born at Dolwyddelen in 1796, had been enticed to Tal y Sarn Quarry in 1821, where he soon married Fanny Edwards, a daughter of one of the men who first opened the Dorothea site.[5] Not only did Jones have access to sound commercial expertise, but his charismatic preaching had created a national personal following (almost a cult in itself) and his participation in the Dorothea scheme created the confidence in the enterprise that was previously wanting.

Soon, enough shares had been sold to pay the deposit and secure the quarry, but the raising of the remaining £1,500 over 18 months proved more difficult in the face of a downturn in the slate trade. Jones practically single-handedly saved the day by canvassing friends and relations, being particularly successful amongst the Methodists at Llangernyw, Denbighshire, where he had been a farm labourer.

The first two years (1849-51) of trading for the new Dorothea Slate Company were not particularly auspicious, with insufficient development capital and a lack of managerial and commercial experience in the face of a depressed market creating despondency amongst the members. With the dismissal of the founding manager and chief promoter (William Owen, Hafodlas) in 1851, the 'Welsh Company' turned to John Jones as its only salvation, a thankless task which he accepted probably as the sole alternative to closing the concern and the loss of all his own and others' savings.

The consequence was that John Jones became all things to all men and suffered accordingly. Attempting to save the Dorothea enterprise would have created sufficient problems in itself, but the additional demands of the

Methodist cause, including long preaching tours on horseback throughout the Principality was a burden beyond even the capabilities of the seraph of Tal y Sarn.

Unsurprisingly, John Jones's ministry suffered from the long hours spent at the quarry, and with his (probably correct) policy of cutting the quarrymen's pay and numbers to balance the books, both the local community and the religious establishment railed against him. Accused by his former sycophants of having become a man of the world, Jones became an isolated figure. Thus, it is not surprising that his biographer described Jones's period as Dorothea manager as a low point in his life.[6]

Without any hint of irony, and in a most extraordinary phraseology to modern readers, Jones' biographer appears almost to relish his subject's near-fatal accident on a new haulage incline at the quarry in 1852 or 1853, which he escaped with only a badly damaged foot. Credited as a double divine intervention, the visit of the Almighty to Dorothea in the guise of metal fatigue on a chain link-pin saw Jones relinquishing active managership of the works to John Robyns, a senior Methodist deacon of Fron. Jones resumed his preaching for a while, but went into decline and died in 1857.

Under John Robyns, even with the increase in trade by the late 1850s, Dorothea was generating little profit and virtually no dividends, and was unsuccessfully offered for sale.[7] Moreover, excuses did not wear in the early 1860s when continuing disappointing results flew in the face of roaring trade and a four-year waiting-list for slates. Most of the old guard, including the widowed Mrs Fanny Jones, sold out of the concern by 1864, and almost all the shares were purchased at a fourfold premium by her son-in-law, John Williams of Llangernyw, in the third turning point in the history of the Dorothea Quarry. With the appointment of the outstanding J.J. Evans as manager in 1864, the tide turned, and the golden age of Dorothea began, when it became known to the quarrymen as 'Canaan' - the land of milk and honey. John Jones was vindicated and his detractors who had sold their shares lost out on the bonanza of two decades of large dividends.

The Painting

The Dorothea Quarry[8] (Plate 1) is privately owned by a member of the family which ran Dorothea until its closure in 1970. It is an oil painting on canvas, measuring 80cm by 52.5cm, a landscape view of the Dorothea Quarry from the

---

[5]   Thomas Edwards, sometime agent for Turner at Pen y Bryn and at Ffestiniog.
[6]   Owen Thomas, *Cofiant y Parch. John Jones Tal y Sarn* (Wrexham, 1874) t. 687-698.
[7]   CRO: X/Dorothea 5; 915; 916.
[8]   The painting is untitled and unattributed; it is referred to here as *The Dorothea Quarry* for convenience's sake.

Plate 1 The Dorothea Quarry, *by an unknown artist.*

north-west, from a vantage-point on the Gallt y Fedw hillside just north of the hamlet and farm of Tal y Sarn Uchaf. However, it is an impossible view in that it looks both east (left) and west simultaneously so as to cover the whole of the quarry in sufficient closeness for detail. Thus perspectives are warped so that the features are to some degree incorrectly related to each other if placed on a map.

An analysis of the content gives a date in the 1850s, based on visual evidence compared to quarry archive material, which is scanty for this period. The very latest date it can be is 1860-61, when the reopening of the No.1 pit and the opening of the new No.5 pit would have created a very different scene. This date can be set back to 1857 if a resolution to create a transporter water-balance in place of one of the illustrated powered inclines is accepted as having been implemented.[9] Whilst it is not impossible that it dates from the end of the Turner period in 1848-9, there is no precedence for such a painting having been commissioned on such an occasion or at the start of a new concern. In view of the rarity of such pictures, we are looking for an auspicious reason for its painting which lies within our time-frame. The most likely candidate would have been to mark the retirement of the Rev. John Jones

from the concern, which would also tie in with the handing-down of the painting through the family on the branch that kept its association with the quarry. A date of about 1854-5 would correlate well with the contents.

Visual analysis

The content of the painting is analysed below by considering the technical and architectural details of the structures therein so as to identify form and function where possible, correlating the evidence to contemporary maps, surviving documents and archaeological site evidence. The numbers and letters by which features are identified refer to Fig. 1 and to the map Fig. 2.

1. Foreground

(A) road

The road shown in the foreground was the turnpike from Rhyd Ddu and Nantlle to the Caernarfon/Porthmadog road at Pen y Groes. The original route, shown on an estate map of 1813, ran to the south across the middle of the Dorothea quarry site,[10] but it had been moved to the course

---

[9] CRO: X/Dorothea 1, minutes 6 Feb 1857.
[10] CRO: X/Maps/437/11.

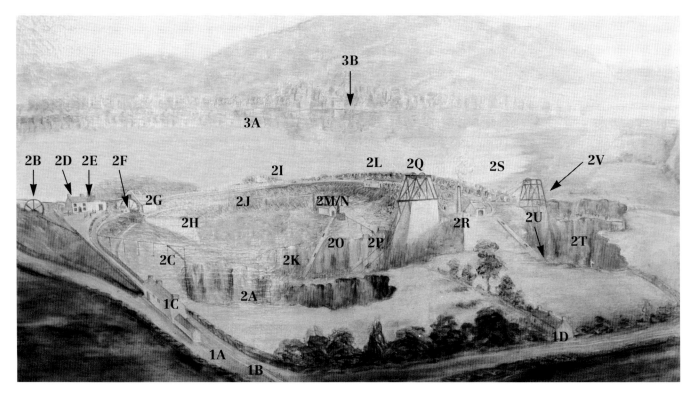

Fig 1 *Dorothea Quarry – features identified.*

shown in the painting by 1840.[11] In 1885 the route to the east (left) of the Commercial Inn was deviated northwards to allow the Dorothea Upper Pit to expand, and its present course is a second northerly deviation.[12] The road to the west (right) of the railway crossing has now almost completely disappeared. Most of the portion illustrated was quarried away in the 1930s-40s, having been replaced by a new road - the present B4418 - which completely bypasses the quarries, because part of the old route collapsed into the Dorothea Quarry in 1924.

(B) the Nantlle Railway

This 3' 6" gauge horse-drawn public railway to Caernarfon was opened in 1828, and this huge improvement in transport facilities was probably a vital factor in William Turner's decision to commence the development of the Dorothea site in the same year. The trackbed shown in the picture was the original course of the railway, of which almost nothing now remains at this location except near the road crossing. The painting accurately shows the line entering the quarry site, but fails to show the continuation of the main line eastwards (left) to its official terminus at the nearby Cloddfa'r Lôn Quarry,

from which a private tramway continued to the Pen yr Orsedd Quarry. In 1885 a new course was constructed due east (left) along the foreground, making the road crossing redundant, so as to allow the expansion of the Dorothea Upper Pit.

(C) the Commercial Inn

This was perhaps built and operated by the Nantlle Railway Company.[13] Its license was revoked in the 1880s as a result of objections by a local teetotal society,[14] and subsequently trade was continued here for several years as a temperance hotel. By the first years of the twentieth century, the 'Temperance' had closed, and in 1907 a landslide precipitated the redundant building into the Dorothea pit.

(D) cottages

These two cottages of unknown date were jointly named 'Tai newyddion' ('new houses') on the 1861 census, but were colloquially known as 'Tai lawr' (probably meaning single-floor houses). They were occupied until the early 1930s, but were destroyed during the northerly expansion of the Dorothea pits in the late 1930s.

---

[11] CRO: tithe map, parish of Llandwrog.
[12] CRO: X/Dorothea 1142.
[13] James Boyd, *Narrow Gauge Railways in North Caernarvonshire* (Oakwood, 1981) p. 86.
[14] CRO: X/Dorothea 1488.

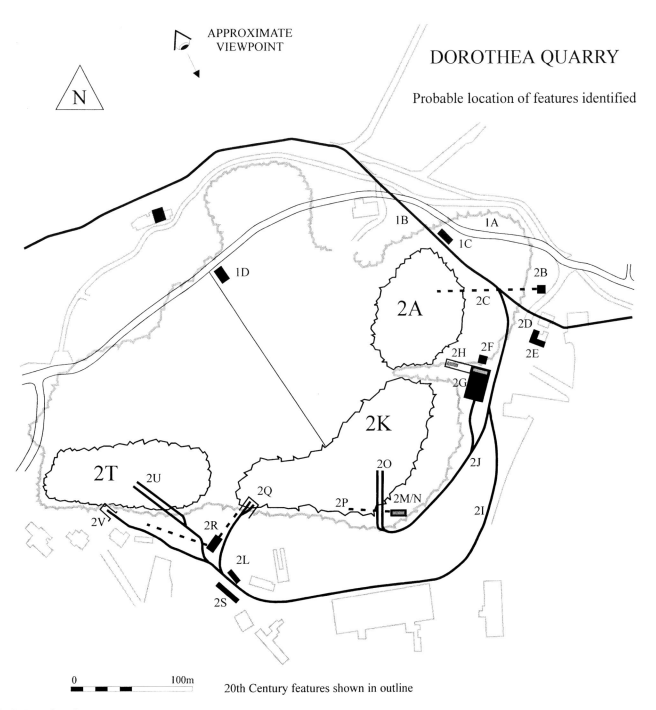

APPROXIMATE
VIEWPOINT

N

DOROTHEA QUARRY

Probable location of features identified

0   100m

20th Century features shown in outline

Fig 2 *Dorothea Quarry.*

2. The Quarry

(A) Upper Pit (Pit No.1 or Old/Upper Quarry, later Quarry A)

This was the oldest pit on the Dorothea site, first opened in the early 1820s. It was abandoned around 1840 because it was thought to be worked out, and consequently other pits were opened elsewhere on the site. The southern face of this quarry was a dolerite dyke, separating it from Pit No.2, and a portion of this can be seen jutting out into the present quarry. The pit must have been deeper than the more modern pits to the west, explaining why it was still being pumped in the 1850s. When the pit was reworked from 1860 to 1901, it was expanded to the north and north-east, forcing the deviation of the Nantlle Railway and Turnpike road (see above). The Upper Pit subsequently

Plate 2
The Dorothea Quarry, by
*an unknown artist
(detail) – features 1A-C,
2A-H.*

Plate 3 *The poor quality
of this photograph is
compensated by being
the only known
photograph to show
Melin Griffith, c. 1910.*

served as a repository for spoil from newer workings opened in the field in the foreground of the picture.

(B) waterwheel on hill (upper waterwheel)

This was the first or upper wheel in the Dorothea series, working the pumps in the Upper Pit. The wheel illustrated is a six-spoked backshot, fed by water flowing in a timber launder apparently supported on timber legs. It is unclear whether the illustrated waterwheel was the 28' diameter one occupying this site in later years, or was its predecessor, because the orientation differs from the 1888 OS map and the construction of the wheel pit does not match that shown on a photograph of *c.*1910. The water supply entered the quarry site just to the north (left) of the wheel, crossing the road on a timber aqueduct, which survived until the 1930s.

(C) pump rods to Upper Pit

The picture shows the pumps in the Upper Pit connected to the upper waterwheel by the standard equipment of reciprocating rods which would have been operated from a crank on the wheel axle. This line of rods was supported on timber legs and connected to the pump by a T-bob. Although the basic system is represented in the picture, the details are inaccurate, especially at the bob-end. The detail of how the rods crossed over or under the railway is also unclear, and the arrangements for disposing of the pumped water are not shown.

(D) front-facing house (Dorothea Cottage)

This building was erected in the 1830s as a house for the quarry manager. It was superseded in the 1870s by a new residence on a riverside site south of the quarry complex, when the old house was divided into two cottages rented to workmen, the last occupation being in the 1970s. The shell of this building is one of the few features in the painting that survives today.

(E) second house - end-on view

The Dorothea Quarry had a resident 'engineer' (most probably the steam winding engine driver) by the late 1840s, and it is almost certain that he lived in the south-facing house. It was demolished *c.*1860 to make way for a winding engine room serving the reopened Upper Pit.[15]

(F) small building by slab mill

No reference has been found to this building, which has the appearance of a weighbridge office, of which there were a number at the quarry in the 1850s.[16]

(G) slab mill (Melin Griffith)

Colloquially named Melin Griffith in later years, this mill was constructed by Turner and Co. in the mid-1840s to exploit a seam of grey-green slate which was not suitable for roofing slates, but which made excellent slabs. The representation of this building, containing two saws and one planing machine, correlates well with later photographs. The 28' diameter driving waterwheel appears to have been backshot and seems to have eight spokes. Its feed appears to come from a branch of the upper wheel feed, via a timber launder on tall timber legs,

although it is likely that the wheel was latterly fed from the tail-race of the upper wheel.[17] The mill tail-race is shown on a lower bank, flowing around to the lower waterwheel, and this arrangement continued until the demise of the slab mill and lower waterwheel in the first decade of the present century (see Plate3).

(H) bastion in front of slab mill

This rectangular structure, built out of the hillside below the slab mill, is shown as supporting a waterwheel, the top of which can just be seen. This wheel was in a position to receive water from the slab mill wheel but the tail-race as illustrated flows along the lower bank to the haulage wheel instead. The best conclusion that explains the details shown is that the bastion wheel must have been disused by the 1850s, a fact supported by the lack of plant attached to it, and neither is there a tail-race shown. Consequently, it can be hypothesised that this wheel may have been the original power source for the pumps in the Upper Quarry in the 1830s, superseded by the more powerful upper wheel when the depth of the pit (and consequently the pumping load) increased.

(I) main quarry bank

The main quarry bank, made up of tipped waste material, was located on the southern (far) and eastern (left) side of the pits. The painting shows these waste heaps as three distinct but interlinked portions. The rubbish tip on which the main working area of slate-making shelters was located curves east from three haulage points on the south-west (back, right) side of the quarry. The original (pre-1842) tipping and working bank for the middle pit was on a lower horizon and had been overlaid by more recent debris by the 1850s, and the only portion of the former that is just visible is the location of the winding engine house and smoking chimney. These individual features are described separately below. On the east (left) side of the quarry there are two ill-defined tips jutting out into the lake, with a causeway connecting the railway and slab mill with the main working area. Much of the larger eastern tip is very likely to have been material from the Upper Pit, when worked by Turner and Co. in the 1830s, but its depiction shows a warping of perspective by the artist because this tip as shown would have overspilled the leasehold boundary into another company's property.

(J) lower bank

The representation of a lower tip level creates several problems of interpretation. Its main feature is shown on

[15] CRO: X/Dorothea 1266. The engine at Pit 1 was listed as 'the Peel Wms engine' (see subsections M and N).
[16] CRO: X/Dorothea 911, 915, 916 (sale prospectuses).
[17] CRO: X/Dorothea 1178.

later maps, that is the aqueduct from the slab mill wheel to feed the lower winding and pumping wheel, but there also appears to have been a separate feed along a leat curving on ground level alongside the Nantlle Railway, for which there is no corroboration. A more serious problem is the omission of detail of the tramway connection from the top of the central haulage incline up to the main working bank, which must have been by means of a long sloping ramp (not shown) to near the slab mill.

(K) Middle Pit (Quarry 'B', incorporating a combined Pit No.2 [Twll y weirglodd - 'meadow pit'] and Pit No.3 (Twll Fire - 'Fire [steam engine] pit')

The No.2 pit was opened c.1838 just to the south of the original No.1 pit as a result of the accidental discovery of a valuable blue slate bed during the excavation of a canal. This short waterway was to have been used to transport overburden from a western expansion of the Upper (No.1) Pit for tipping into the lake, but the scheme was abandoned in response to the surprise discovery. The No.3 pit, which had the steam winder prominently illustrated in the painting, was opened to the west of the No.2 opening in 1841-2 because the latter's development had been stalled by adverse geology. No.3 expanded rapidly eastwards and also in depth, and absorbed the No.2 pit into one large working, which had been sunk about 450 feet below bank by its abandonment in 1908.

(L) office

This building survived intact until the 1970s, and was very similar to the representation in the picture (Plate 4). It had a date of 1842 or 1847 inscribed in internal plasterwork of the western and earlier half of the structure. There was latterly a belfry on the west gable and a lean-to addition, but neither is shown in the picture. It was superseded as the main quarry office in the 1860s, but remained in use as the slate inspectors' office until the late 1950s. Some foundations of this building still remain.

(M) large waterwheel and (N) building

This was the lowest and last of the series of waterwheels at Dorothea. It was fed by the tail-race of the slab mill via a long leat coming along the lower bank. This wheel operated pumps in the No.2/3 combined pits, and also probably worked the haulage incline in Quarry No.2, although the details of the drive system are not shown. It may also have at one time worked the haulage incline in Quarry No.4 (see below), alternative or multiple uses of fixed power sources being common in quarrying technology. The present lower waterwheel pit, of unknown

date, is on a different site and alignment to that shown in the picture, the illustrated one having been quarried away by the 1880s (Plate 5).

The purpose of the long building adjacent to the wheel is unclear, but it may have housed the winding gear or even a steam winder for the incline. A steam engine was inspected for possible purchase in 1853 and one had been bought by 1857 for use on a haulage incline.[18] This was an in-house rotative condensing beam engine by Peel Williams, Manchester, having a vertical single cylinder of $26^{1}/_{2}$" bore and 39" stroke, developing 50 horse power at 45 r.p.m. at 50 p.s.i. of steam and 13 p.s.i. of vacuum. Whilst the building is sufficiently large to contain such an engine, no boiler house or chimney can be seen, and it is unfortunate that the painting provides tantalising but unclear evidence for the power sources of both the inclines illustrated.

(O) haulage incline

This incline runs at right angles to the likely power source at its brow, although this was not a technological problem. It is represented as having trucks running on their own wheels rather than on transporters. The incline is, however, drawn on a scale that appears too small for its true size, possibly on purpose. If this painting were a present to John Jones, a too prominent a reminder of his accident on a new haulage incline (possibly this one) in 1852-53 might have distressed the recipient.

Plate 4 *The old office, Dorothea Slate Quarry in June 1975.*

(P) pumps

These pumps serving Quarries Nos. 2, 3 and 4 were located near the water outlet tunnel running through the tips to the lake. The fixed location of this tunnel also dictated the site of the later main (pre-Cornish Engine) pumps, albeit at a slightly different location. The rod drive system working the pumps is similar to that described for the Upper Pit.

---

[18] CRO: X/Dorothea 1, minute of 26 August 1853 re-inspection of second-hand engine; X/Dorothea 1077 (sale prospectus, c. 1857), reference to a proposal to replace the steam winders with a water-balance.

Plate 5
The Dorothea Quarry,
*by an unknown artist
(detail) – features 21-P.*

(Q) winding frame on pyramid

The tall 'pyramid' base erected on the edge of the southern face of the middle quarry was raised about 30 feet above the original tipping bank so as to establish the new higher working level which would maximise the available space for dumping rubble in the lake. The pyramid was a base for a timber headframe supporting a pair of aerial chains leading down into the quarry, these being equivalent to the railway tracks on a conventional inclined plane. A pair of counterworked pulley carriers traversed the chains, being operated themselves by light winding chains counter-wrapped on a drum powered in this case by a steam engine. As one loaded wagon attached to the incoming winding chain ascended, an empty wagon attached to the outgoing winding chain descended the aerial incline. This plant, installed *c.*1843, was a copy of that introduced from Cornwall by an English concern at the adjacent Cloddfa'r Lôn Quarry a year earlier, and similar units continued in use at Dorothea until the late 1950s, although wire ropes had replaced chains in the 1890s.

(R) winder house

This was the first steam winder at Dorothea, powering the chain incline of *c.*1843, discussed above. The engine was a rotative condensing in-house beam engine of unknown make, recorded as having cast iron support columns of a Greek temple pillar design. It had a single vertical cylinder of 21" bore and 48" stroke and developed 50 horse power at 50 r.p.m. on 40 p.s.i. of steam and 13 p.s.i. of vacuum.[19] The engine was erected on the old quarry bank and was gradually encircled by the new higher debris heaps (see above). In later years, if not originally, it was also capable of being connected by a rod drive to the pumps when the waterwheel was out of action through drought or ice. The boiler house as illustrated appears to be on the west side of the engine, which differs from the later arrangement of which remains are still visible. However, this poses no archaeological problem because a Cornish boiler, bought in 1863, was almost certainly a replacement for the original boiler of this engine.[20] The engine was never relocated from its cellar-like location despite a company resolution to this effect in August 1860, and both it and the winding stage were eventually destroyed by a huge rockfall in 1926.

(S) *gwaliau*

A single row of about twenty shelters (in Welsh, *gwaliau*) can be seen on the quarry bank behind the No.3 Pit winder house. Their open fronts are placed away from the prevailing south-westerly winds so as to shelter the teams of slate splitters and dressers. The *gwaliau* were progressively replaced at Dorothea by mills from the 1880s when sawing of slabs was mechanised, and few now survive here.

(T) West Quarry ('No.4' Pit or 'Quarry C' later, colloquially Twll Coch ['Red Pit'])

This was opened in the mid-1840s by Turner and Co., to exploit the purple slate bed which was separated from

---

[19] CRO: X/Dorothea 612, 614.
[20] CRO: X/Dorothea 612.

the older workings by a bed of gritstone, and eventually became the deepest working at Dorothea, 600' below quarry bank. Although it expanded north in later years, the south-west face shown in the painting is virtually identical to its present boundary because development in this direction was halted by poor trade in the 1850s and was never restarted. Subsequently, the South Dorothea Quarry occupied the land to the south, and the Cornish beam engine of 1904-06 was also erected on the south side of the 'C' pit.

(U) haulage incline and building

This structure, which served Pit No.4, has several unexplained features. No record has been discovered for its construction, which probably predates the chain incline (below) and thus served the pit from its opening c.1846. If so, then the incline is almost certainly likely to have been originally powered by water, and the most likely candidate is the lower waterwheel, which is in a direct line with it. Yet as illustrated in the painting, it is possible that the incline was powered from the building at its brow, which suggests a steam engine - although other features suggest otherwise. This building seems to have a large window facing the incline as expected in a winder house, but the only chimney is one on its gable apex which has the appearance of a domestic one and the whole structure seems too small for the second in-house beam engine purchased in the 1850s, thus creating an uncertainty which cannot now be resolved.

(V) winding frame for chain incline

This chain incline was almost certainly a secondary feature in the development of Quarry No.4, and as such is likely to have been installed by the Welsh Company post-1850. The headgear base still exists, and it was within living memory called 'the Pulpit', referring to the folklore that the Rev. John Jones used it as a vantage paint to watch the workers below. The headgear illustrated is virtually identical to that serving the No.3 quarry, and this design persisted at Dorothea into the twentieth century. Unfortunately, the painting does not show clearly the power source for this hoisting equipment. No winding house is visible, and it is very likely that it was powered in tandem with the No.3 chain incline.

Such arrangements were not uncommon in this district, and the No.3 pit winder was definitely sufficiently powerful for the job, ultimately working three such units concurrently.

3. Background

(A) Llyn Nantlle Isaf – the lake

Initially, the lower of the two Nantlle lakes (Richard Wilson's vantage-point for his view of Snowdon) was an asset to the Dorothea Quarry because it provided the works with a capacious site for tipping its waste. However, the lake was to become a perennial nightmare following a huge landslide in 1884, which caused its waters to burst into the workings. The quarry was totally drowned out for over a year until expensive flood defences were constructed, but despite the draining of the lake in 1894-6, winter floodwater collecting in the old basin breached the quarry dams on several occasions thereafter.

(B) Plas Gwernor

The old Gwernor farmhouse, dating from the seventeenth century, is just visible on far side of lake. It was demolished when the new B4418 road was constructed in the 1920s.

Plate 6
The Dorothea Quarry, by an unknown artist (detail) – features 2Q-V.

Conclusion

The painting contains a surprising amount of detail of the quarry and its machinery, and is consequently a valuable historical primary source if used with care.

Although many of the features depicted can be tied in with documentary evidence for the 1850s, there are nonetheless several areas of doubt concerning the accuracy of the painting. However, it must be kept in mind that technological accuracy was not the prime motive of the artist, who was more concerned with capturing the essence of the scene. That he did so with such care for detail can only be ascribed to the likelihood that the painting was a special commission for an important person - possibly the Rev. John Jones Tal y Sarn - and in so doing provided later generations with a remarkable and rare glimpse of a major slate quarry in its early stage of development.

Part (II)

by Peter Lord

The painting of *The Dorothea Quarry* as it was in the 1850s falls within a small *genre* of depictions of industrial scenes in Wales made in the late eighteenth and nineteenth centuries by artists who had not received an academic training. The best parallel for the picture is, perhaps, a pair of drawings made by William Pamplin of the Cyfarthfa Ironworks in about 1800.[21] Pamplin was a gardener in the employ of Richard Crawshay, the owner of Cyfarthfa, though whether the drawings were commissioned by him or done for the gardener's own amusement is unclear. Like the Dorothea painting they provide an important record of the works at a particular stage of its development. They also predict the north-Walian picture in their unselfconscious approach, compared to the works of those few academically-trained painters who turned their attention to industrial subjects, such as John Warwick Smith and Julius Caesar Ibbetson, who painted the Parys copper mines in the late eighteenth century, and Henry Hawkins who painted the Penrhyn slate quarry in 1832.[22] Nevertheless, the painter of the Dorothea picture set the subject in a wider landscape of the lake and the mountains beyond, which suggests some familiarity with academic landscape images and an intention not exclusively documentary. He or she was also familiar with the basic rules of perspective, demonstrated not only by the drawing of built features but also by the effective rendering of the depth between the quarry in the foreground and the mountains beyond. The use of oil paint does not imply a professional artist, since paint was available ready-mixed in tubes from the 1830s, and, furthermore, it was applied in a way not characteristic of a trained painter, like a watercolour wash.

Again echoing the Pamplin drawings of Cyfarthfa, the painter chose to depict the scene from a birds-eye view, an archaic convention of the period *c.*1700, when it marked a transition from a plan-like exposition of the features of a scene to the modern landscape in which the subject is depicted firstly for its visual qualities. However, notwithstanding its scenic background, *The Dorothea Quarry* is essentially an explanatory panorama which strongly suggests that either the artist or the patron had a particular interest in the quarry, almost certainly as a local person and perhaps also as an employee. On the other hand, inaccuracies of technical detail identified by Gwynfor Pierce Jones do not suggest a quarryman.

The artist is most unlikely to have painted the picture on site, since it is, in a sense, abstract. Rather, it will have been constructed at home from imagination and memory, which might account for topographical inaccuracies in the relationship between features, even if some site drawings or photographs of details were used as reference. For the same reason it is not necessary to see *c.*1860 as the last date at which the picture can have been painted. Indeed, working from a strong visual memory, often many years after a subject depicted has ceased to exist, is characteristic of many naive painters.

Extending the date at which the painting may have been produced permits a possible attribution of the work to John Parry, 'Ap Idwal', the only artist known to me whose style, locale and dates all approximately fit the requirements. Parry, who died in the Bangor workhouse in 1904, was from Dyffryn Ogwen but worked for clients over a wider area. Although he was a professional, in the sense that he charged small sums for his work, his style was naive, and it is not impossible that he painted *The Dorothea Quarry*, perhaps early in his career. However, I think it more likely that it was the work of a local amateur, very familiar with the site but not necessarily working there. Whoever the painter, he or she provided industrial historians with a valuable document, and a wider audience with a glimpse of the Snowdonia often shunned by academically trained artists in their explorations, where industrial communities and unsullied landscape met.

[21] Illustrated in Peter Lord, *The Visual Culture of Wales: Industrial Society* (Cardiff, 1998), pp.18, 68.
[22] *Ibid.*, pp.22-6, 80-1.

New Light on Ty Mawr Ynys y Pandy

by Dr Michael Lewis

The great slab mill which belonged to Gorsedda quarry is widely known and properly admired, but the inspiration behind its architecture and the layout of its machines has always been enigmatic. Recent research and archaeological work, however, have revealed something of its architectural context and of the location and nature of its machinery.

Introduction

Gorsedda quarry at the head of Cwmystradllyn is the classic example in the slate industry of mis-invested capital, of vast sums spent on such peripherals as a magnificent slab mill, tramway and village before the rock itself was thoroughly tested. When the slate was found to be worthless, vast sums of money had been poured down the drain. But the fiasco, however financially damaging to the investors, has bequeathed to the industrial archaeologist a quarry untouched since about 1865, a unique settlement, and a mill that boasts what is arguably the finest architecture in the industry.

Serious working at Gorsedda, hitherto the scene only of intermittent scratchings, began in 1854 when an unlimited company was formed, which three years later became the Bangor & Portmadoc Slate & Slate Slab Co Ltd with a capital (very large for those days) of £105,000, later increased to £125,500. First and last there were never more than fourteen shareholders, all Englishmen. Apart from a couple of stockbrokers, most were railway directors, engineers or contractors connected with the Lancashire & Yorkshire or the London Brighton & South Coast Railways.[1] Their interest may at least in part have been in securing a ready supply of slates and slabs for their own stations and goods sheds. Shipments of slate, however, totalled a derisory 8,685 tons, averaging 668 tons a year, with a peak of 2,148 tons in 1860.[2] The workforce, at least until 1859, numbered 200 to 250.[3] The manager was Edwyn John Jeffery Dixon, a native of Plymouth who had previously been engineer and manager of Bryn Hafod y Wern quarry

at Bethesda. The tramway from the quarry to Porthmadog was built by James (later Sir James) Brunlees (1816-92), a railway engineer who later achieved considerable renown.[4] By 1865 all the capital and all the revenue from sales (which can hardly have exceeded £20,000) had been spent, and in 1865 or 1866 production ceased. While detailed documentation other than formal company papers is virtually non-existent, there are several contemporary verdicts on the Gorsedda debacle. They agree that the protagonists were not fraudulent, but naive. 'Everything that capital could do was done to make a slate quarry ... but they were fighting against the decrees of Nature, and lost the battle. There was no quarry there.'[5]

History

Fascinating though they are, the quarry, the village of Treforys with its thirty-six semi-detached cottages, and the tramway, just over eight miles long on a gauge of 3',[6] are not our present concern. But the mill, Ty Mawr, is.[7] Roofing slates were made, as was normal at that time, entirely by hand in the quarry, but the manufacture of slabs required power. Adequate water supplies are not available at the quarry, and permission was first obtained to build a mill on the Afon Henwy just below Llyn Cwmystradllyn.[8] In the event, a better site was found nearly two miles below the quarry, on the farm of Ynysypandy Uchaf and beside the road up the valley (SH550433, Fig 1).[9] In 1855 the whole farm was bought,[10] and in 1856-7 the mill was built in tandem with the tramway. Both were finished by May 1857 when 'roofing slates, sawed and planed flooring slabs,

[1] Details of finances and shareholders from PRO BT 31/235/755.

[2] UWB Searell 4 (5a); DRO ZM/1199.

[3] *Mining Journal* 1856, p. 340, 1857, p. 127; DRO ZDBE/58 f.24.

[4] *Minutes of Proceedings of Institution of Civil Engineers* 24, 1865, pp. 386-7.

[5] *Mining Journal* 1868, p. 511.

[6] A history of the tramway and its successor, not entirely reliable, is given in J. I. C. Boyd, *Narrow Gauge Railways in South Caernarvonshire* (Lingfield, 1972), pp.15-51.

[7] Surprisingly little has been published about it. After thirty-five years, the present writer would wish to recant a few of the opinions expressed in Elisabeth Beazley and M. J. T. Lewis, 'Great Welsh Slate Mill', *Architectural Review* 806, 1964, pp. 300-302. Boyd, *op. cit.*, p. 39 gives a brief and misleading description, Alun John Richards, *A Gazeteer of the Welsh Slate Industry* (Capel Garmon, 1991), p. 103 a brief and good one.

[8] UWB Carter Vincent 2647-8, CRO XBJC 349. Henwy is the proper name of the river, though nowadays it is often called Afon Cwmystradllyn.

[9] Despite the name, there is no evidence that a fulling mill ever existed here. The farm was probably a daughter settlement of the Ynysypandy opposite the present Bryncir woollen mill.

[10] CRO XBJC 349.

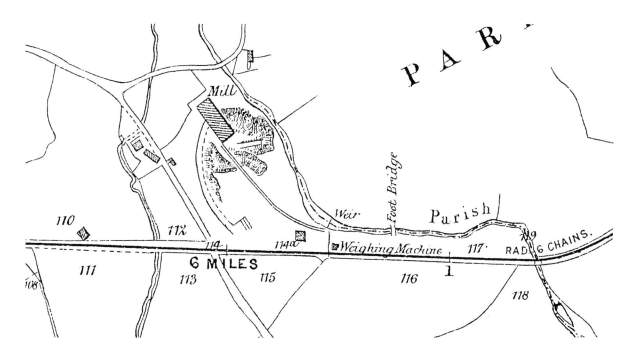

Fig 1 *Site plan, from deposited plans of Gorseddau Junction & Portmadoc Railways, 1871 (north is to top right)*

window sills, or slate slabs for general purposes' were first advertised for sale.[11] The extravagance of the mill caught the contemporary imagination. It was described as 'an extensive machine house full of first-class machinery which alone cost £10,000',[12] and 'The company spent an enormous capital in building a huge factory ... The machine room is built regardless of expense, and is supplied with a large number of sawing, planing and dressing machines'.[13]

After closure, the company's assets were bought for a song by the Prince of Wales quarry at the head of Cwm Pennant,[14] which extended and converted the tramway to 2' gauge as the Gorseddau Junction & Portmadoc Railways. The new owners sold the farm to Owen Roberts and John Lewis of Porthmadog,[15] but retained Ty Mawr which, they proclaimed, they intended to use as a mill again, but never did so.[16] Tradition says that thereafter there was considerable social use of the first floor as a kind of unofficial village hall, and around 1888, when Capel Saron nearby was being rebuilt, it hosted chapel services and even an eisteddfod.[17] It is said that about 1890 it was

stripped by R. M. Greaves who used the pitchpine timbers in rebuilding Wern;[18] but this testimony is dubious because, according to a contemporary sketch (Fig. 2) by the local schoolmaster, the mill was not unroofed until 1906, when the rebuilding of Wern had long been completed.[19] In fact in 1894 the mill was sold for £100 to Owen Roberts ironmonger (who already owned the farm) and Robert Isaac engineer, both of Porthmadog.[20] Demolition was in their blood (in 1896 they scrapped the Porthmadog end of the tramway[21]), and it was probably they who stripped Ty Mawr. Thereafter it has stood as an empty and impressive shell. In 1981, as a Scheduled Ancient Monument, it was bought by the National Park and most sympathetically consolidated (and safety railings installed) by Richard Cuthbertson.

Design and layout

Ty Mawr is a building with a dual fascination, architectural and technical. Perched on the edge of the river gorge, its impressive silhouette, reminiscent of a

[11] *Carnarvon & Denbigh Herald* 16 May 1857.
[12] *Mining Journal* 1873, p. 1407.
[13] *Practical Magazine* 3, 1874, p. 82, copying and slightly altering a passage from *Carnarvon & Denbigh Herald* 14 June 1873.
[14] CRO XBJC 349, BJC Addl 4/1306.
[15] CRO XBJC 349.
[16] *Mining Journal* 1873, p. 1407; 1875, pp. 631, 902.
[17] Information from Mrs Hughes, Braich y Bîg, per Dr G. P. Jones; Dewi Williams, *Chwareli a Chloddfeydd yn y Pennant* (Caernarfon, 1986), t. 8
[18] Information from the late Col. Martyn Williams-Ellis.
[19] The OS 25-inch revision of 1899 shows the mill still roofed, while the revision of 1913 shows it unroofed.
[20] CRO XBJC Addl 4/1306.
[21] CRO XBJC Addl 4/49.

Ty Mawr Prys pandy: Cwmstradllyn
Fel yr oedd cyn ei ddidoi yn Ionawr: 1906.

Fig 2 *Mill in 1906 from north east. Tailrace arch at bottom.*

ruined abbey, is totally unexpected in such a landscape. It comprises two storeys, an attic, and in the north-west quarter a basement dictated by the fall of the land (Plates 1-4). All were lit by ranks of round-arched windows and doorways. Those at the centre and ends of the first floor on the south side are larger than the rest, a not uncommon conceit in polite architecture; the east gable is adorned with an elaborately bordered window and roundel and capped with a dummy chimney; the west gable sports a corbel that perhaps carried a flagpole. Abutting the basement to north and west is a terrace enclosed by a wall with decorative capping. It is a large building, 34.8 by 11.7m inside on the ground floor or almost exactly in the ratio of 3 : 1.

In this multi-storey layout and imposing design, Ty Mawr is totally untypical of slate quarry architecture. The closest parallels for the layout are a few water-powered writing slate mills: the Newborough at Blaenau Ffestiniog, built before 1879 apparently as a flour mill, which rose to four floors at the water-wheel end;[22] and four at Clwt y Bont (Glandinorwig, Deiniolen, Caerffynnon and Caerhedyn), apparently all two-storey and built between 1851 and 1860,[23] But if some of these exceeded Ty Mawr in size, their architectural pretensions were minimal. Otherwise the ordinary quarry slab mill, like the slate mill for sawing blocks for splitting which was just coming in during the 1850s, was invariably single-storey and only very rarely, as at Rhosydd 9 mill of probably 1859, did it have embellishments such as round-headed doorways.

---

[22] Photograph in Ann Rhydderch, *Blaenau Ffestiniog* (Caernarfon, 1979), fig. 18.
[23] Information from Meurig Owen; some photographs in GAS XS/1998.

Plate 1

Mill from Gorsedda Tramway, 1960.

Plate 2

Mill from south east with upper tramway embankment and lower tramway immediately on its left. 1960.

We are not told who designed Ty Mawr, but we can hazard a guess. Among industrial buildings this rhythm of large round-headed windows is most commonly found not, as has been suggested, in textile mills but in foundries and engineering workshops;[24] and the proprietors and servants of Gorsedda quarry included railway engineers and contractors who must have been very familiar with the style. In particular, James Brunlees, the engineer of the tramway, had in his younger days worked under Sir John Hawkshaw on the Manchester & Leeds Railway, soon to become a constituent of the Lancashire & Yorkshire. He must have been involved from 1845 onwards in building the locomotive and carriage works at Miles Platting, which centred on a three-storey building with fenestration very

[24] Compare for example the following buildings: Craig and Donald's machine tool works of 1845 at Johnstone in Renfrewshire (John Butt, Ian L. Donnachie and John R. Hume, *Industrial History in Pictures: Scotland* [Newton Abbot, 1968], p. 80); the Dowlais roll lathe shop of about 1856 (John A. Owen, *The History of the Dowlais Iron Works* [Risca, 1977], f.p. 88); Gill and Bray's foundry at Tavistock (Frank Booker, *The Industrial Archaeology of the Tamar Valley* [Newton Abbot, 1967], p. 224); the Long Shop at Garrett's engineering works at Leiston of 1853 (*Industrial Archaeology* 4, 1969, p. 346); even, more locally, the now-demolished Britannia Foundry at Porthmadog of 1851 (Myfanwy Morris, *Porthmadog* [Caernarfon, n.d.], fig. 9), though in the last two cases only the fronts, not the sides, had round-headed openings.

Plate 3
*Mill from south west
with tramways entering
on right, 1963.*

similar to Ty Mawr.[25] We may therefore with some confidence ascribe to Brunlees the design of the mill. We also know the name of the actual builder: Evan Jones, a stonemason born in Clynnog who after a spell working at Ffestiniog had settled at Garn Dolbenmaen, where he built most of the houses on London Road.[26]

Water tapped from a weir a short distance upstream passed along a tunnel to the centre of the south wall, where it turned north to enter the mill and drive an overshot or pitchback wheel about 7.7m in diameter, wholly below floor level. The tail-race discharged straight back into the river, and by means of ring gears the wheel turned two drive shafts. One ran eastwards along a slot, 3.76m deep below the ground floor, which continued for another 6m outside the east wall (Plates 5-6); the shaft was carried in bearings mounted on transverse stone blocks well above the slot floor. The other shaft ran westwards through the basement. From a point just above the mill to the south, the tramway sent off two curved branches, one on an embankment entering the first floor by a central door, the other immediately below it entering the ground floor just to the west (Plates 1-3). Most waste left the mill through the east door to the tips beyond, though a little was tipped westwards from the lower tramway.

Considerable effort has gone into recording the structure. The late Douglas Hague made a splendid if not entirely accurate isometric drawing, and more recently Peter Hughes has meticulously measured and drawn plans and details,[27] although problems of access to the higher parts have so far precluded really good elevations being made. The exact nature and location of the machinery, however, and the flow of materials through the mill, has never been clear. There were necessarily subsidiary drives running more or less vertically up from the drive shafts, and we know that there were saw tables, planers and dressing machines. But how many, and where? Were blocks from the quarry brought into the top floor for processing there and lowered to the ground floor for further work, the finished products leaving by the lower tramway? Or was the flow the other way round? Or were the two floors broadly independent of each other? Locating heavy and doubtless vibrating machinery on a purely timber floor, however massive, is not good engineering practice; so were the large machines below and the small ones above? Where did the tramways run inside, and where was the hoist which surely existed? The only visible clues to such questions lie in features like the drive shaft slot, recesses in the walls for line shafts (two of them in the blocking of windows which points to secondary modifications), and a curious low square opening in the east wall beside the doorway leading to the tips (Plate 6).

---

[25] Photograph in J. Marshall, *The Lancashire & Yorkshire Railway*, vol. 2 (Newton Abbot, 1970), p. 89. I am indebted to Peter Hay for this reference.
[26] Information from his great-grandson, Owen Williams, Ymwlch Lodge, per Dewi Williams.
[27] Both are unpublished.

Plate 4 *Basement looking north west, 1974. Courtesy Susan Smith-Uncles*

Archaeological investigation

Since examination of the visible structure could take one so far but no further, it became clear that to enhance understanding of this enigmatic building, and specifically of the nature and location of its machines and internal tramways, it would be necessary to look for evidence immediately below the turf on the mill floor. Scheduled Monument Consent was therefore obtained from Cadw, and between 13 and 25 August 1995 the floor of the mill was examined by members of a course in practical industrial archaeology at the Snowdonia National Park Study Centre, Plas Tan y Bwlch.[28] The southern half of the ground floor was divided into eight roughly equal areas (S1-S8, see Fig. 3), and the north-eastern quarter and the basement into three each (N1-N3 and B1-B3); the drive

shaft slot was already divided into four unequal bays (D1-D4) by transverse bearing stones. Lack of time prevented investigation of B2 or B3, but all the other areas were entirely or selectively deturfed and examined. Although levels were taken from the weir, consideration of the water-wheel and its launder was not on the agenda.

The lower limit of investigation was the original mill floor, which consists of made-up ground comprising random chunks of country rock topped with small-calibre stones and gravel and a thin layer of yellowy-brown clay. This floor forms a distinctive – and usually the only – horizon. It lies at a depth below the turf which varies from about 5cm in N1-N3 to a general 15-25cm in S1-S8, and is level except for places where compaction of the fill has created slight depressions. There is no indication that, apart from the slabs to be listed later, the floor had ever

Plate 5 *Interior looking west, drive shaft slot and bridging slabs in foreground, 1974. Courtesy Susan Smith-Uncles*

---

[28] The tutors were Merfyn Williams and the writer, and the participants, full- and part-time, were Ian Devine, Hazel Fleming, Dave Gunning, Celia Hancock, Peter Hay, Moyra Holm, Stuart Holm, Griff Jones, Jon Knowles, Chris Lester, Hywel Lewis, Naomi Lewis, Dafydd Price, Peter Swift and Ian Walters.

Plate 6 *East end looking west, 1974. Centre, drive shaft slot and low-level doorway out to partly-infilled extention. Far left, square opening.*
Courtesy T. R. Smith

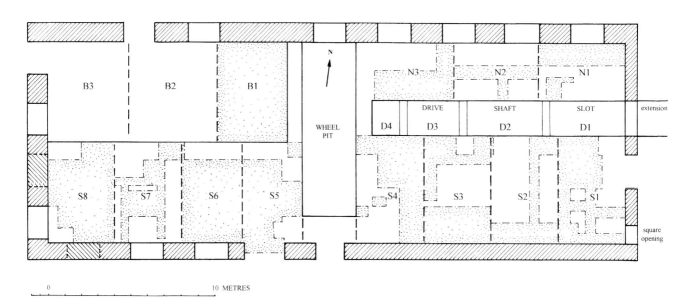

Fig 3 *Key plan, basement and ground floor. Areas investigated stippled.*

been flagged, although the wheel-pit was doubtless floored over with timber.

Above the floor, four types of material may be distinguished:

1. Saw waste consists of a very fine and pure grey dust, turning to a clay when damp. It may contain sawn ends of slate which fell off the saw table. When uncontaminated it is easily recognisable.

2. Planer waste is slightly coarser: a mixture of dust and small flakes (rarely more than 4cm in length and very thin) removed from the slab by the planing process. It may contain sawn and planed fragments of slabs which broke during the planing. When uncontaminated, it too is easily recognised.

3. Dressing waste consists of a mixture of larger pieces: flakes and chippings up to 20cm or more derived from trimming the slates, roofing slates which broke in the dressing, and sawn blocks which proved unsuitable for splitting.

4. Demolition debris consists of a miscellany of material: fragments of country rock or mortared slate dislodged from the structure when the timbers were removed, pieces of lime mortar, and broken roofing slates, all with an admixture of soil accumulated since the mill was unroofed.

The material lying on the original floor was deposited in at least two distinct phases — the working life of the mill, and the stripping of the roof and floors — but in general it was much disturbed and intermingled. Demolition debris was everywhere (though least plentiful in N1-N3), and everywhere it was mixed with processing waste; but

though this waste was thoroughly contaminated, its calibre offered broad clues to its original nature (see Fig. 4).

S3-S6 and N3 contained quite fine waste, nowhere fine enough to class as saw waste but compatible with planer waste, with few broken or rejected slabs. In N3 there was a patch of uncontaminated planer waste adjacent to the window, outside which was a larger dump of planer waste.

The northern third of S1-S2 and S7-S8, and to a lesser extent N1-N2, contained fine waste and many sawn ends; in S7 there was a small uncontaminated patch of saw waste.

The southern two-thirds of S1-S2 and S7-S8 comprised dressing waste, with considerable quantities of sawn ends.

In the basement and drive-shaft slot the material was much less disturbed. In B1 the demolition debris was extensive, and towards the south it overlay a clear-cut layer of planer waste.

In the drive shaft slot the original floor was covered with a deliberate but crude layer of rough thin slates, perhaps to assist the shovelling up of waste (Fig. 5a). On this, in D2, was a layer about 10cm thick of uncontaminated saw waste and the usual sawn ends from the primary cutting of blocks. In D3, spilling through into D4, was a layer between 7 and 30cm thick of uncontaminated planer waste, and many offcuts and broken fragments of relatively thin and narrow slabs between 5 and 25cm wide, sawn parallel on opposite edges and planed on one face. More examples of these were found on the tips, sometimes with the edges polished.

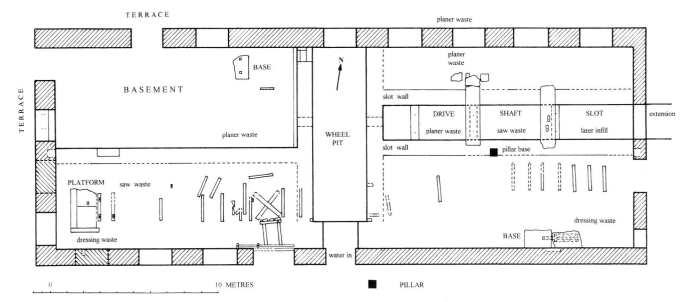

Fig 4 *Features revealed, basement and ground floor.*

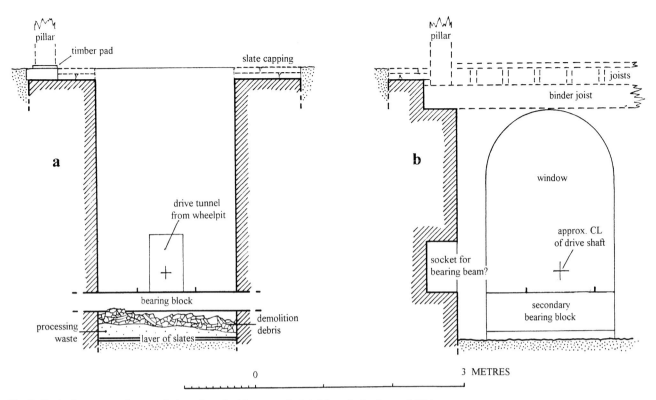

Fig 5 *Typical cross sections and elevations looking west in (a) drive shaft slot and (b) basement.*

Above all this processing waste, and clearly demarcated from it, was demolition debris containing considerable quantities of rough mortared slabs varying from hand-size to 2m long. In D1, where the slot has been partly filled with rubble in association with the blocking of the doorway through to the extension beyond, the floor was not reached.

Sockets in all four walls show that the first floor consisted of longitudinal joists resting on massive transverse binder joists about 35 by 30cm, which in turn were supported in mid-span by a longitudinal timber running the length of the mill. This timber must have been carried at intervals on vertical pillars, but the slab base for only one such was found, central in the eastern half of the mill and resting on the southern wall of the drive shaft slot. The absence of holes in the slab and the presence on it of a timber pad 36cm square imply that the pillar was of wood, not iron. Gaps in the masonry at the corresponding point in the western half, and on either side of the wheelpit, suggest that similar pillar bases there have been robbed. The walls of the drive shaft slot, built like the rest of the mill of large blocks of country rock, were topped with pieces of slate set in mortar to create a level bedding for slabs or, more probably, timbers; when the timbers were stripped, many of these pieces of slate fell into the slot, as already mentioned.

Three other bases were located. Against the south wall in areas S1 and S2 is a pair of slabs with holding-down bolts (or the holes for bolts) for a small machine, and rust-marks from its pedestal. In the wall above it are two recesses for a drive, both apparently secondary (Plate 9). Near the west wall in S8 is a low and crudely-built platform of mortared slabs, once surrounded on at least two sides by timber baulks (Plate 10). Being made of sawn ends, it is clearly secondary, but because a tramway butts up centrally to its east face it must belong to the working life of the mill. It too has an associated drive shaft recess beside it in the blocking of a window, which confirms its secondary nature. Near the north wall of B1 is a slab bearing the rust-marks from two feet, apparently of a machine, but no holes. Otherwise there is no sign of machine bases in the floor. In addition, two long slabs bridge the drive shaft slot, the eastern one having a number of holes crudely drilled through it, the western one being undrilled (Plate 5). In the slot below the latter was another broken slab, and 2m further east a fragment of perhaps a fourth; both these broken slabs also have holes in. A few small slabs north of the western bridge may be *in situ*.

A number of exceedingly rotten tramway sleepers were found *in situ* (Plate 7), and three more were located by depressions in the turf but not exposed. A few of the sleepers still carried chairs set at 3ft gauge. Areas S3-S4,

Plate 7 *Sleepers of diverging tracks in S6, just west of turntable, 1995.*

where sleepers would be expected, were almost innocent of them, perhaps because they were removed along with the rails. Just inside the south door of the mill the foundation of a turntable was found (Plate 10), marked by a diagonal cross of supporting timbers and by four or five tracks diverging from it: (a) south, to the lower tramway entering the south door; (b) west, to end against the platform; (c) north-west to run alongside the south wall of the basement, although few traces survived; (d) possibly a short stub north to the basement wall; and (e) east across the wheel-pit, although the precise method of bridging this is not clear. In the eastern half of the mill, this last tramway swung north to run along the southern edge of the drive shaft slot and out through the east door to the tip. A long east-west timber inside the south doorway carried a single rail set in ordinary chairs as a track for a sliding door. It used to be thought that of the two curved branches running from the Gorsedda Tramway to the mill, the one to the first

floor ran uphill and the one to the ground floor downhill; but levelling reveals that both ran down, one at 1 in 500, the other at 1 in 35.

Apart from ubiquitous nails and spikes and fragments of window glass in the demolition debris, the ground floor and basement yielded only a few loose tramway chairs, a short length of rail not *in situ*, a few small and unidentifiable fragments of cast iron from machine frames, some broken files, and a fragment of slate roll ridge (probably from the roof, not a product of the mill). In D2 and D3, however, at the base of the demolition debris, were fragments of spokes and rims from belt wheels of two sizes: 30cm (1') diameter by 9cm (3$\frac{1}{2}$") wide, and 122cm (4') diameter by 22cm (8$\frac{1}{2}$") wide; the holder plate for a planer blade; two clutch forks; a small keyed hub; a flanged wheel probably from a saw table; part of a small lubricator bottle; various small and unidentifiable pieces of iron; and (in D1 and D2) clinker and mortared firebricks.

Plate 8 *Turntable site from south. Basement beyond, wheel-pit on right, 1995.*

Interpretation

The paucity of rubbish on the ground floor suggests that, except for dressing waste in the southern corners, processing waste was not allowed to accumulate to any great depth; and what there was on the floor was much disturbed, first by the scrapmen breaking up the machines, next by the demolition men stripping the timbers (who further complicated matters by bringing down processing waste from the first floor), and perhaps finally by the men consolidating the structure in 1981. Hence the absence of any stratification, except in the basement and the drive shaft slot where these operations had much less effect. The distribution of the different kinds of waste, however, both in contaminated form on the ground floor and in pure form in the basement and drive shaft slot, gives some idea of what kind of machines were where.

In the eastern half of the mill the concentration of processing waste on the floor of the drive shaft slot, and of

iron fragments lying on top of this waste, shows that there were machines mounted astride the slot. The mortared and levelled capping on top of its walls, and the absence of evidence for machine bases and for concentrated processing waste on either side of the walls, suggest that the machines' feet rested on timbers on the walls and that their waste fell, or was brushed, straight into the slot, although some planing waste was shovelled out of a window to the north. It is clear enough that over D3 and D4 was a planer, and over D2 was a saw table. Whether there was a third machine over D1 or the saw table partly extended over it, is matter for debate.

If these machines were aligned north-south across the slot and stood on top of its walls (2m between inner faces, 3.9m between outer faces) their tables, about half their total length, would be exceptionally short. Their drive pedestals, too, would be central over the slot and without support, since the holes in the bridging slab are too crude for this purpose. More likely, therefore, the machines were aligned longitudinally east-west and parallel to the tramway, as in Holland's first slate mill at Blaenau Ffestiniog which was closely contemporary with Ty Mawr. We may indeed hazard a guess at the type of the saw table. In 1852, before he became manager of Gorsedda, Dixon had joined forces with Arthur J. Dodson, proprietor of Coetmor Quarry at Bethesda, in taking out a patent for a variety of devices for quarrying and dressing slate.[29] Some can only be described as bizarre, and others are irrelevant to us. Their planer, for instance, had a tool which planed the whole width of the slab at once; in contrast, the tool holder found in the drive shaft slot was of normal width and presumably came from a 'standard' planer.

Their sawing machine for slabs, however, is of distinct interest (Fig. 6). Its proportions as shown in the unscaled patent drawing would not suit Ty Mawr because, if the machine was wide enough to straddle the slot lengthways, its table would be awkwardly high above the ground. But all the other features fit. The table is adjustable for height, and the shaft carries two adjustable circular blades for making parallel cuts (Fig. 6). Although another machine described in the patent has the blades cutting upwards through a slot in the table, in this case they are mounted above the table. As a result, if the table is set a trifle too low, the slab is not completely cut through. This conforms with the evidence of waste on site. The patent describes blades which are 'cut or notched on their edges with a chisel or tool, and present an edge somewhat like a file'. They are continuously and automatically sharpened by a cam-operated chisel which throws a burr each side instead of the set of the usual teeth and curiously, according to the

[29] Patent no. 14165. I am indebted to Jon Knowles for a copy of the specification and drawings.

Plate 9
Secondary base and drive recess in S1, looking south, 1995.

Plate 10
Secondary platform in S8, looking north, 1995.

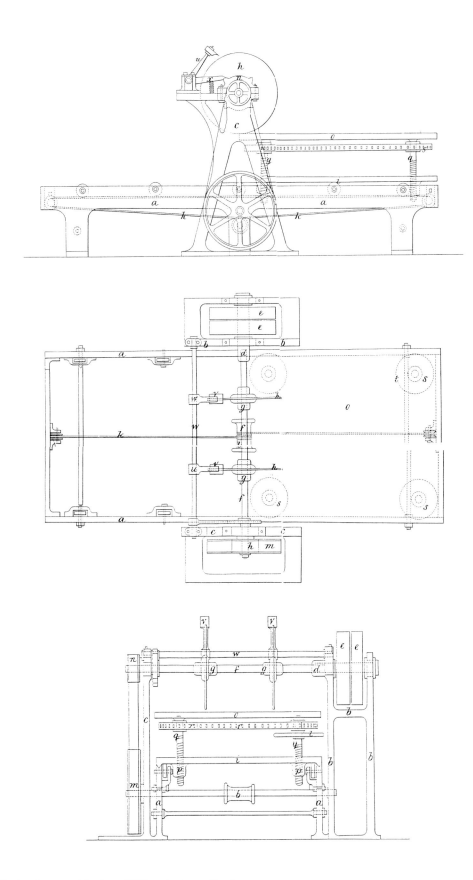

Fig 6 *Dixon and Dodson's saw table, from 1852 patent specification.*

drawings, always strikes the same four points on the circumference. A small proportion of the sawn waste at Ty Mawr displays quite smooth edges, undoubtedly cut by a circular saw, but one which has left marks much shallower and finer-pitched than the relatively prominent ridges made by the usual toothed blade. This would be the effect of the Dixon and Dodson patent.

It may therefore be suggested that Ty Mawr was equipped with at least one Dixon and Dodson saw roughly 5m long; and, because of the mix of normal and smooth-edged sawn ends, that its file-type blades, proving unsatisfactory, were replaced by toothed blades. With machines of this sort of length there is hardly room over the slot for more than two, one saw and one planer. Except under the machines and where the belts came up, the slot would be floored over, presumably with planks because slabs would be all too easily broken if a block were dropped on them. The bridging slabs that survive would find themselves under the machines, and with their crude holes may be anchors added to hold pulleys to tension the feed chain under the saw table, which from the drawings looks all too liable to slip. Because the drive shaft evidently ran to, or at least nearly to, the east end of the mill, each machine evidently had its own drive from it, with a fast and loose pulley. This is not the place to debate the precise arrangement of each drive beyond remarking that, in the absence of any sign of foot bearings, a geared take-off seems unlikely. The only alternative is a belt drive in, presumably, two stages, which on this orientation of the machines would at some point have to be taken through a right angle.

It is hardly good practice (though it is paralleled elsewhere) to drop waste on to a drive shaft and its bearings, even if they were boxed in. But since it was evidently intended that waste should be dumped here, provision must have been made to remove it. The external extension to the slot, connected to it by a full-sized doorway, runs about 6m beyond the mill and its floor, though now deeply buried, presumably lies at the same depth (about 3.8m) as the floor of the slot. It has been suggested that its purpose was to allow the drive shaft to be withdrawn for maintenance; but because the shaft would certainly be built up of coupled sections and would need little attention, this seems improbable. More likely the extension allowed the removal of the waste from the slot. It could accommodate a flight of steps, relatively shallow for the sake of men carrying heavy baskets or buckets. Its sides were no doubt originally walled up to ground level. To keep sheep out of the mill after it was stripped, a number of doorways and windows were blocked with dry stone walls (removed in 1981), the material for which was probably robbed from the upper courses of the extension. The fill

behind these courses, left unsupported, subsequently collapsed inwards and created the present crater-like appearance.

In the western half of the mill the evidence is more slender, but tends to suggest a symmetrical arrangement, with a saw table to the west (attested by the many sawn ends and saw waste in S7-S8) and a planer to the east (evidenced by the planer waste fallen into the basement). The fact that the south wall of the basement lies further south than that of the slot may indicate either that these machines were set further south, or were wider, than the others. No trace was found in the basement of supports corresponding to the north wall of the slot, which suggests that the binder joists between basement and ground floor were hefty enough to carry half the weight of the machines above; indeed two of the three binders, from the size of the sockets which they occupied in the south wall, were apparently doubled at that end for extra strength.

What happened in the basement is less clear. The terrace outside, on to which its two doors opened, had no road or rail access and could be reached only on foot. There was internal access from the ground floor in the north-east corner of the basement, where the top of a flight of steps can be seen, and the slab base against the north wall may possibly be connected with the foot of the stairs. The floor is at the same depth as the drive shaft slot (about 3.76m: Fig. 5b) below the ground floor, and the sill of the west window, as bolt holes show, carried the end bearing for a drive shaft symmetrical to that in the slot. But in B1, the only section deturfed, no trace appeared of an intermediate bearing block corresponding to those in the slot. There are however low-level sockets in the south wall which could have carried one end of bearing timbers. The shaft also underwent alterations: the bearing mounted on the crudely-raised window sill is clearly not original, and the shaft must once have been either shorter or carried in a different bearing. As in the drive shaft slot, waste was evidently allowed to fall into the basement, from where it seems to have been shovelled over the edge of the terrace to the north. Otherwise the basement's function, if any, remains unknown. Conceivably, if the drive shaft were suitably partitioned off, it housed the office of the company, whose registered address was at the mill throughout its working life; unless the office was in the attic, where the roof trusses would obstruct most other activity.

There are concentrations of dressing waste in the south-east and south-west corners. The shape of the pedestal which once sat on the base near the south-eastern corner, and its position close against a wall, are not reminiscent of a dressing machine. Perhaps, rather, it carried a saw-sharpening machine; and because it was clearly secondary, its insertion might have coincided with

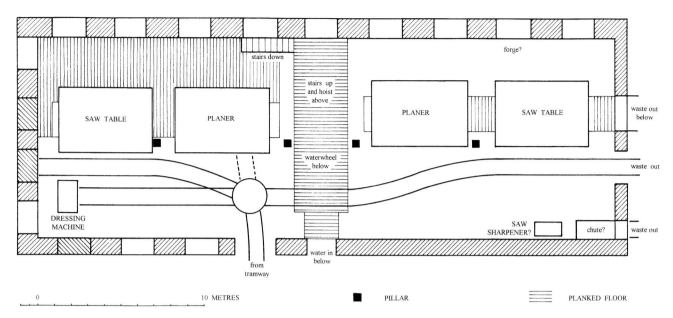

Fig 7 *Suggested reconstruction of layout, ground floor only.*

the change, postulated above, from file-edged to ordinary toothed saws. The spillage of dressing waste in this corner is not necessarily connected with a machine here. Splitting and dressing into roofing slates of usable sawn ends and of slabs which broke in the processing could have taken place anywhere on the first floor. If the resulting waste were shot down a chute in the south-eastern corner, through the square opening on the ground floor — which shows no sign of ever having a window frame — and into a rubbish wagon outside, spillages from the chute would account for the waste here. The platform in the south-western corner, which is also a secondary feature, probably carried another and later dressing machine, the waste (or most of it) falling straight into a wagon on the tramway which abutted it.

The firebricks and clinker concentrated in D1-D2 imply the existence close by of a forge for sharpening tools and the like. Since no trace was found against the south wall, it was perhaps against the north wall in the area not investigated between the second and third window from the east. The stairs to the first floor were most likely over the wheelpit, as was the hoist, handy for the two planers. Fig. 7 attempts an outline reconstruction of the layout of machines and tramways on the ground floor.

It seems increasingly likely, therefore, that the ground floor ultimately contained four heavy machines and two light ones. Raw blocks would enter the mill by the lower tramway, and the internal tramways would deliver them to the saw tables and remove waste through the east door. Movement of slabs from saw table to planer would be by

hand. Simple slabs — sills, gravestones and the like — which required only sawing and planing could be made solely on the ground floor and sent out, as their raw material had arrived, by the lower tramway.

The principal clue to the purpose of the first floor lies in the thin and narrow slabs with planed surface and polished edges, a few of which were also filed on their ends. They were evidently a speciality, perhaps even a major product, of the mill. They were not for writing slates (which were invariably split but not planed, let alone polished on the edges); indeed the cleavage of Gorsedda slate is too uneven for the purpose. Their intended use can be deduced not only from similar examples elsewhere but from Owen Morris's compendious list of uses for slabs, written at Porthmadog even as Ty Mawr was being built:

> The numerous purposes to which these slabs are devoted is astonishing. They are extensively used as pavement, for the flooring of houses, warehouses, terraces, balconies, conservatories, &c., for steps, for the lining of damp walls, for wash-houses, and baths, powder magazines, larders, wine-cellars and dairies. They are also manufactured into cisterns, tanks, wine-coolers, bread pickling and pig-feeding troughs, urinals, filters, head and foot stones for graves, toombs [*sic*] and monuments, clock faces, and sun dials. Chimney pieces are largely made of slate, varying in price from six shillings to twenty five pounds.[30]

---

[30] Owen Morris, *Portmadoc and its Resources* (Blaenau Ffestiniog, 1856), p.48.

Of this catalogue, the chimney pieces — fire surrounds and mantlepieces — precisely match the offcuts found. As the upper price limit implies, they could be very elaborate. They would need equipment for finishing: benches for drilling assembly holes and perhaps for carving, polishing machines, and possibly (as already suggested) a dressing machine for turning breakages into roofing slates. They would also need considerable space for laying out and fitting the components. All this, it seems likely, was the function of the first floor. On this supposition, the machines here were few and light, and the apparent and puzzling impropriety of imposing heavy machinery and heavy slate blocks on a purely timber floor disappears. Nor need the hoist be a heavy-duty one, since only light slabs had to be lifted from below. Finished products would depart by the upper tramway, and the unexpectedly spacious area some 11m wide at the end of the embankment immediately outside the exit door might even have served as a small stackyard.

While much of this reconstruction is necessarily hypothetical and can only be put forward tentatively, it does seem in accord with the evidence both of the visible structure and from beneath the turf.

Acknowledgements

I owe thanks for their labours in investigating the mill floor to all those involved in the project in 1995; for permission to reproduce photographs to Tim Smith and Susan Smith-Uncles; and for information, discussion and help of all manner of kinds to Peter Crew, David Gwyn, Peter Hay, Gwynfor Pierce Jones, Jon Knowles, Meurig Owen, Dewi Williams, and above all to Merfyn Williams.

Book Reviews

Griff R. Jones, *Hafodlas Slate Quarry* (privately published, 1998)

ISBN 0 9533692, 209 pp., softback, £12:50.

Hafodlas Slate Quarry near Betws y Coed is one of the more impressive archaeological survivors from the hey-day of the industry, making use of a bewildering variety of machinery, much of it installed for the most part by the galaxy of engineering talent which ran the place throughout the 1860s. The quarry's history has found a worthy chronicler in Griff Jones. Many readers of *Industrial Gwynedd* will be familiar with his work, but unless they have been fortunate enough to see some of the advance copies of the plans of this site, which he and his fellow-workers have been recording for a number of years, this book will come as a revelation. The measured drawings set new standards of industrial archaeology recording; they are not only detailed but easy to follow - works of art in their own right. It is backed up by extensive archival research, and even though the quarry breathed its last as long ago as 1929 Griff has taped reminiscences from surviving workmen, which have amplified the written and the material evidence.

The book is attractively produced, though here and there one comes across evidence that the author has not been particularly well-served by his printers in terms of printing and proof-reading. This is a pity, but in no sense detracts from the volume, which is a delight. Congratulations are therefore due not only to Griff himself but to his team - to Dafydd Price, to the late Arthur Mornant Roberts, Bill Jones and to Elfed Williams.

* * * *

Alun John Richards, *The Slate Quarries of Pembrokeshire* (Gwasg Carreg Gwalch, 1998)

ISBN 0 86381 484 0, 196 pp., softback, £5:50.

Further proof that study of the slate industry is at last breaking free from the Gwynedd heartlands is Alun Richards' most recent book. Most Pembrokeshire slate quarries were small but, as the author bids us remember, a vital source of livelihood in this thinly-populated part of Wales. As ever, Alun Richards packs in much information in a small space, and has performed a valuable service in researching and writing up this study. It follows the familiar Gwasg Carreg Gwalch format, though the photographs are slightly better than usual. This book can be warmly recommended.

* * * *

M.J.T. Lewis, *Millstone and Hammer: The Origins of Water Power* (University of Hull Press, 1997)

ISBN 0 85858 657 X, 180 pp., softback.

No-one familiar with the industrial archaeology of Gwynedd needs to be reminded of the way in which water-power was by no means universally eclipsed by steam as a prime mover in the modern period. What may come as a surprise is its antiquity - certainly on the evidence which Michael Lewis has amassed. The vertical water-wheel, the force pump and other devices all derive from the astonishing spate of invention and experiment at the Museum in Alexandra during the third century b.c.

Dr Lewis's background in the classics is evident in his use of literary sources, but this is no dry text-book for the senior common room - the style throughout is readable and accessible, as he takes us from the Egypt of the Ptolemies to China, Samarqand and to Moorish Spain. Though he modestly describes this volume as a contribution to a continuing debate, the crucial argument that the water-driven industrial mill dates back to the Roman empire rather than to the Middle Ages seems to a non-specialist such as the present reviewer to have been set forth very convincingly. Archaeology has confirmed a water-wheel-driven stamp mill from a Roman context at Dolaucothi; it seems highly probable that further excavation will confirm Dr Lewis's belief that water-power was far more important and far more developed in antiquity than has been hitherto supposed.

* * * *

Gwilym R. Roberts, *New Lives in the Valley: Slate Quarries and Quarry Villages in North Wales, New York and Vermont, 1850-1920* (Farmington, Maine, 1998)

ISBN X12345, pp. 470, hardback, £15:99.

There was scarcely a family in North Wales in the nineteenth century untouched by emigration - and who could fail to be tempted to make the crossing oneself on hearing of success stories such as that of Hugh W. Hughes, the 'Granville Slate King'? Born in Nazareth, in Llanllyfni in 1836, he made his way to America at the age of twenty-one, to work in the lead mines of Dodgeville and the copper mines of Lake Superior, before reaching the Vermont slate belt. By the 1880s he was a wealthy quarry proprietor, the embodiment of success in his astrakhan coat who took his vacations at Saratoga Springs and at Bermuda, and who kept a stud of horses in the stables of the finest house in Granville - all this without ever learning to read or write in either Welsh or English. Others, it need hardly be said, came to America and found little in the way of a promised land, though Welshmen had generally worked their way to managerial positions by the time successive waves of immigrants entered the industry - Ruthenians, Italians, Irish. These communities have also had their historians - Eva Macura, described as 'chronicler of Slovak life in Granville' is photographed standing next to a prominent car-sticker reading 'We support our boys in Vietnam.'

The ethnic and religious mix that Professor Roberts describes evidently made for a lively community, and the story is a fascinating one. To Welsh eyes, the quarries look strange - for the most parts open pits, à la Nantlle, so Nantlle-type technology is much in evidence in the form of chain inclines and blondins, though the earliest type of lifting arrangement was evidently a derrick powered by a horse-whim, for which there is little evidence in Wales. Very few quarries seem to have made use of internal rail systems, since only horses and carts are evident on most of the photographs. In a way it is a pity that Professor Roberts has not told us more about work in the quarries themselves, and though there is much interesting material here, as a social or industrial study it lacks the densely-argued texture of some of the best work on the Welsh industry. But it is well worth reading to put the slate industry within its proper global context, and above all to learn something of the experience of the families from Bethesda, Bethel, Blaenau or Nantlle who experienced the trauma of leaving their homes for a new life thousands of miles away.

* * * *

Peter Lord, *The Visual Culture of Wales: Industrial Society* (Cardiff, 1998)
ISBN 0-7083- 1496-1, pp. 272, hardback, £25:00.

Readers of this journal will be able to judge Peter Lord's work at first hand; *The Dorothea Quarry* is surely one of the very few paintings of industrial landscapes to have escaped his notice in this remarkable and beautifully produced volume. Its theme is the paintings, drawings, photographs, cartoons and films of industrial Wales, from the illustrations of the Cardiganshire lead mines which accompanied the *Fodinae Regales* in 1670 to the work of Howard Roberts in the 1960s. Many of these come from the naive tradition which Peter Lord has rescued not so much from the condescension of posterity as from its ignorance - he has uncovered over the last ten years a richness of style and subject-matter of which hardly anyone was aware, and these now take their rightful place alongside the academicians' work. Inevitably, the illustrations are the glory of this book, but this is one to be read as well - its style is scholarly, yet with no trace of the etiolated academicism of much art-historical writing. At £25 it is a bargain.

Notes for contributors/ nodiadau i gyfrannwyr

Contributions should be sent to the editor at Nant y Felin, Ffordd Llanllyfni, Pen y Groes, Caernarfon, Gwynedd, LL54 6LY (note the new address). They may be of any length, though it is difficult to find room for articles over 7,000 words. The editor cannot be responsible for the text of submissions. If at all possible, they should be on 3½" disc. The system we use is WordPerfect 6.1, and the font is Times New Roman in 12-point (10 point for quotations separate from the main body of text). An initial summary of the article for inclusion as part of the published text is helpful, and Welsh-language articles should be followed by a brief outline of their contents in English.

Structure

If you wish to number sections and sub-sections, rather than use continuous prose, the form we use is as follows (example taken from vol. one, article on Penscoins incline):

The Unloading Shed, Drumhouse and Incline

(i.e. capitals, in bold)

The drumhouse and unloading shed have been ...

1. THE UNLOADING SHED

The unloading shed is a rectangular building ...

(A) tip area

In the north-east corner of the building is a small tip ...

Further subdivisions of (A) may be indicated by lower case roman numbers within brackets, immediately followed by text, thus:

(i)

Style

Spelling: to follow *Concise Oxford Dictionary of Current English* or *Geiriadur yr Academi.*

Quotations: to be enclosed within double inverted commas, quotations within quotations to be enclosed within single inverted commas.

References: wherever appropriate, sources should be referenced. The journal uses footnotes rather than endnotes or the Harvard system of author-date reference within the text. Typescripts submitted can, of course, be adapted by the editor if your computer system does not enable you to do this. A **printed source** should appear thus in a footnote:

¹ Sir John Wynne, *History of the Gwydir Family and Memoirs,* ed. J.Gwynfor Jones (Llandysyl, 1990), *passim.*

Manuscript sources thus:

⁶ NLW 4983. *(followed by page or folio recto-verso reference where appropriate).*

Articles in journals thus:

⁹ Robert Williams, "Hunangofiant Chwarelwr", *Cymru* XIX, Awst 1900, t. 88.

(Note that in the case of Welsh-language references in English-language articles, dates and page reference should be in Welsh).

Newspapers thus:

North Wales Gazette, 31 January 1811, p. 3, col. a.

Measurements: these may be given in metric or imperial lengths, as appropriate.

Numbers: figures should be used for measurements, *e.g.* 200 metres, but time and figures under 100 should be expressed in words, hyphenated thus: twenty-seven.

Dates: in the main body of the text these are given as in the footnote reference above, thus: 31 January 1811.

Illustrations: maps, plans and diagrams to accompany articles are very welcome; contributors should note the page-size of the journal (9½" x 7½", 250mm x 190mm). They should be referred to in the text as (Fig. 1 *etc.*). The editorial board will gladly arrange assistance in the preparation of illustrations.

Photographs: these should ideally be black-and-white, and the caption should be marked on the back in soft pencil. This should include the call-number of those from libraries, archives, etc. They should be referred to in the text as (Plate 1 *etc.*).

For **book reviews,** information should be given in the following order: author, title, editor, publisher, place of publication, date of publication, number of volumes, number of pages, whether illustrated, ISBN number, whether hardback or softback or both, and the price, thus:

Thomas Pennant, *A Tour in Wales,* ed. R. Paul Evans (Bridge Books, Wrexham, 1991) 2 vols., 1083pp., illustrations. ISBN for 2 vol. set, 1-872424-14-7, ISBN for vol. 1, 1-872424-15-5, hardback, 1083 pp. £45.

This example has been chosen as the most complicated; in practice few books have both an author and an editor, or have two ISBN numbers.

Any contributor who wishes guidance is welcome to contact the editor, Nant y Felin, Ffordd Llanllyfni, Pen y Groes, Caernarfon, Gwynedd, LL54 6LY.